"You'd do *anything* for a story," he sneered

Cass was bewildered. If Lucien had spoken to Lionel, then he knew she hadn't slept with the man. What *was* he going on about?

Lucien continued, "I remember when you thought I was your target. You played me so cleverly—dangling your pretty self before my eyes, advancing, retreating. What a pity I missed out on the final stages of the campaign. I'd love to know what you'd planned...."

"It wasn't like that!" Cass protested, then suspiciously asked, "What *did* Lionel say to you?"

"He said," Lucien went on with deliberation, "that he didn't normally give interviews, but when a girl had as much to offer as you did, he was willing to make an exception."

Cass was bereft of speech. Lionel Halliday had lied, and Lucien had believed him!

DAPHNE CLAIR
is also the author of these

Harlequin Romances

and these

Harlequin Presents

Many of these books are available at your local bookseller.

For a free catalog listing all titles currently available,
send your name and address to:

HARLEQUIN READER SERVICE
1440 South Priest Drive, Tempe, AZ 85281
Canadian address: Stratford, Ontario N5A 6W2

Pacific Pretence

by

DAPHNE CLAIR

Harlequin Books

TORONTO • NEW YORK • LOS ANGELES • LONDON
AMSTERDAM • PARIS • SYDNEY • HAMBURG
STOCKHOLM • ATHENS • TOKYO • MILAN

Original hardcover edition published in 1982
by Mills & Boon Limited

ISBN 0-373-02516-5

Harlequin Romance first edition December 1982

CHAPTER ONE

THE ship's band was playing a medley of popular music as Cass edged her way into the crowd on the brightly lit deck. Already dozens of frail paper streamers were stretched between ship and shore, the wellwishers on the walkway outside the terminal waving and calling last-minute admonitions and goodbyes to their friends and relatives. There were no tearful farewells here. The ship was a cruise vessel, and the vast majority of the passengers would be returning to Sydney in just over two weeks' time, after visiting several Pacific islands. The leavetaking was a happy occasion.

The huge vessel began to move so quietly that at first Cass didn't realise they had cast off. Gradually the streamers strained and snapped, to a chorus of mock-groans, laughter and cheers, and the figures on the quay became small and doll-like as the ship swung away, the tugs invisibly turning it to head out to sea.

The famous Opera House, fabulously lit, a glittering series of glassed arches reflecting the sea and the city lights, slid by, and two seagulls flew level with the deck, eerily ghostlike as they kept pace with the ship. Tall buildings slipped behind and the lights on the shore became smaller and farther away, until at last the final headland was passed, a pale cliff plunging into the black sea. And night closed in on them as the ship began a gentle dipping and heaving, slowly heading into the open Pacific.

There were few people left on the open deck, now. The sea-breeze had become nippy, and Cass had pulled up the collar of her padded nylon jacket as she hunched over the solid wooden rail for a final glimpse of land. The band had long since packed up and gone inside, and the only sound was the slap and swish of the water against the ship's side, as Cass turned reluctantly away from the rail. Even the engines seemed to operate silently, although there was a very faint vibration beneath her feet as she pulled open the wooden door and stepped into the carpeted luxury inside.

A babel of voices came from the bar nearby, in the bow, and she hesitated, wondering if she should go in there. She supposed she should start looking . . .

But wandering into a bar on her own on the first night at sea didn't appeal. And she had scarcely seen her cabin yet, only stopping there long enough to leave her bag and see that her cabin-mate, whoever she was, had not yet arrived. The cabin had been roomier than Cass had expected, with two wardrobes, two easy chairs and ample drawer space, and even the upper berth of the pair looked wide and soft.

It had been a long, tiring day, starting with the flight from New Zealand, and made longer by the two hours time difference between Auckland and Sydney. She had had to put her watch back on the plane. She considered whether she should be exploring the ship, watching out for the man she must find, but the thought of bed was infinitely tempting.

She found the broad stairway and started down, casting curious glances at the other passengers she met on the way to B-Deck, where her cabin was. Everyone smiled in a friendly fashion, and she automatically returned their greetings. She didn't think that Lionel Halliday was among them. All the men seemed to be attached to family groups, and her information was that Mr Halliday was definitely unattached.

By the time she had descended six flights of stairs, she was slightly dizzy. She clung for a moment or two to the stair rail, getting her breath back, and trying to remember whether she had to turn left or right for her own cabin.

'Are you all right?' a man's voice asked her, and she looked into a fair, boyish face and smiled at the concern and quick admiration she saw in the blue eyes meeting hers.

'I'm fine,' she said. 'Just getting my bearings, that's all.'

'What's your cabin number?' he asked quickly.

Cass hesitated, and the young man laughed. 'I'm quite harmless,' he told her. 'Odd numbers that side, even numbers over here,' he added, grinning.

'Thanks.' Cass grinned a little ruefully herself, and moved away from the stairs.

'I'll see you around,' the young man called after her hopefully, and she turned to say, 'Yes, thank you again.'

He waved and bounded up the stairs.

Cass was still smiling to herself as she inserted her key and pushed open the door of the cabin. *That* certainly wasn't Mr Halliday, she told herself. Too young, and too fair. Also too friendly, she decided. By all accounts, Lionel Halliday wasn't the friendly type.

The girl kneeling in front of an open suitcase on the floor by the beds turned at her entrance. Cass saw rather unruly dark curls, a vivid, painted mouth that changed from a siren pout to a surprisingly friendly smile, and brown eyes that held a spark of suppressed excitement.

Holding some folded clothing in one hand, the girl scrambled to her feet. 'You must be Cass Reynolds. I looked at the labels on your baggage—hope you don't mind? I'm Lois—Lois Lescot. Which bunk do you want? You *were* here first, but you don't seem to have bagged one.'

'I don't mind,' Cass assured her. 'You choose, if you like.'

'Honest? Then can I have the top one?' Catching Cass's look of surprise, she added, 'My sister and I had bunks when we were kids, but Kathy always had the top one because she was the eldest. I've never got over wanting to sleep in the top bunk for a change.'

Cass laughed. 'It's all yours.'

'Goody! Isn't this fabulous? I always wanted to go on a cruise. I've been saving for this for ages. You, too?'

'Actually, no,' Cass admitted. 'I was given the cruise as a sort of belated twenty-first birthday present.'

'Wow! Lucky you! Who do you know that's throwing around holiday cruises for birthday presents?' Lois demanded. Then, suddenly rolling her eyes heavenward, she added quickly, 'Whoops! Sorry—that's nosy, I suppose. Kathy's always telling me to mind my tongue.'

'Not at all, that's all right. My aunt is a constant traveller, and she'd booked the cruise for herself. But she slipped and broke her leg a few weeks ago, and rather than cancel the whole thing, she transferred the ticket to me. My birthday was really months ago, but she was away in South America at the time. This was a nice surprise.'

'I'll say! Your aunt sounds fabulous.'

'She is,' Cass agreed. Aunt Claudine had always been something of a fairytale character to her. She wrote very successful mystery novels with a touch of romance, travelling the world in search of exotic backgrounds, and returning once or twice a year to her native New Zealand, descending on her relatives with gifts of silks and strangely wrought carvings or, in Cass's case, colourfully garbed dolls and an assortment of picture postcards. She was Cass's godmother and her father's only sister. Even after his sudden death when Cass was ten, Claudine had kept up her visits to his widow and only daughter. Cass's mother had remarried when Cass was nineteen and working as a very new reporter on one of Auckland's daily newspapers. A year later her stepfather had been transferred to Wellington by his firm, and Cass, liking her work and not wanting to leave the city in which she had grown up, had persuaded her mother to let her stay and move into a flat with friends.

Her mother and stepfather had come up from Wellington to celebrate Cass's twenty-first birthday by taking her out to dinner, and since then she had spent a long weekend with them, but their lives had diverged from hers and she was no longer dependent on them, much as she loved her mother.

She had counted herself lucky to be taken on to the staff of a new metropolitan magazine by an editor who allowed his mostly young team to put forward their own ideas for stories, and encouraged them to follow through. He could, though, become tough and uncompromising, as she had discovered when Aunt Claudine had offered her this trip. Unimpressed by her excitement and eagerness to take up the offer, he had refused to give her leave of absence, saying that if she wanted to go she could resign, but there was no guarantee that her job would be open when she returned.

'But Rudy!' she wailed disbelievingly. 'It's only for a couple of weeks——'

'Nearly three,' he told her tersely.

'Well, all right, nearly three. I'd be due for holidays——'

'You've been here less than six months.'

'Well, of course! We all have—the magazine isn't even six months old yet!'

'Exactly. Do you know how many magazines have gone down the drain in the last ten years? If this one is to get off the ground we all have to work really hard, for a long time. We can't afford a gap in the staffing just now. If you do go, I'll have to replace you. No one gets a holiday until Christmas. Sorry, Cass.'

Rudy bent his head to the layout spread on his desk, and picked up a ruler and blue pencil. Obviously, that was his last word. Cass swallowed, feeling her disappointment like a hard, cold lump in her throat, and left his office. She didn't want to give up her job. And Aunt Claudine, who had been so pleased to be able to give Cass her magnificent present, was going to be disappointed, too.

Cass put off telling her, wondering if even now there was some way out of the dilemma. She tackled Rudy again, suggesting that a story on a cruise ship could go down well with readers, and that there was plenty of scope for travel pieces in the ship's itinerary.

He looked thoughtful, but after a moment regretfully shook his head. 'We've got a travel writer,' he reminded her. 'I don't want to step on his toes, and besides, most of the islands have been done before—ad nauseam.'

'Well, the ship itself——' she offered eagerly.

'We ran a piece on cruises just a few weeks ago, remember? We don't want to repeat ourselves.'

'I could find a different angle——'

'No, it wouldn't work. Forget it.'

But two days later he came by her desk with some papers in his hand, and said, 'That cruise ship of yours—what date is it leaving Sydney?'

'The twenty-fourth,' she said, puzzled, not daring to be hopeful.

Rudy glanced at the papers he was holding and said, 'Come into my office. I want to talk to you.'

She followed him, thoroughly mystified, and he sat at his desk and frowned abstractedly at his clasped hands for several seconds before he glanced up at her.

'Ever heard of Lionel Halliday?' he asked.

Cass thought for a moment. 'Property?' she said. 'Isn't he a sort of property magnate?'

'Dead right. New Zealand's youngest millionaire, according to some usually reliable sources. He lives in Auckland, and I've been trying to set up an interview with him for our "Cameo" page. There's a lot of interest in him at the moment, since he managed to pull his irons out of the fire before the Magnum group collapsed with all that attendant publicity. A lot of our readers were involved in that, one way or another—Magnum had fingers in several pies. So they're interested in the man who saved himself from the mess some of them got caught in.'

'They're out for his blood, aren't they?' said Cass. 'Wasn't there some suggestion that the company wouldn't have folded if he had stood by it?'

'It's arguable whether a delay in his withdrawal of funds and assets could have prevented the collapse,' Rudy agreed. 'Or whether, in fact, his action directly or indirectly *caused* the disaster. He's not popular. And he's not courting publicity—not that *that's* new. He always has kept a low profile, refused interviews, shied away from photographs. But lately he's been doubly hard to find. Now, I've been tipped off that his doctor's told him to take a holiday, a nice relaxing holiday away from newspapers and TV and high finance. And guess what?'

Cass wasn't slow on the uptake. 'A cruise?' she said.

'Of course, a nice, leisurely, restful cruise around the Islands. They say it's about the most relaxing holiday there is.'

'Tell me about it when you get back,' said Rudy, grinning faintly.

'You mean I can go?'

'There's a condition.'

'Of course. A story on Lionel Halliday.'

'An interview, Cass.'

'*Interview?* You just said he's supposed to be resting. And he doesn't like publicity at any time, you said. How am I supposed to——'

'Look, a story I can get any time—there are files, you know. An interview is what I want.'

'But, Rudy, I can't just ring up the poor man and demand an interview!'

'You're a reporter, aren't you? Find a way.'

'Supposing I can't?'

'Don't tell me "can't", my girl. You're either a reporter or you're not. If you come back without the interview, you come back without a job. I'm not letting you go just to gallivant about the Pacific having a good time. You go on assignment or not at all. And you'd better deliver the goods.'

'You're not paying my fare!' Cass protested stormily.

'I'm doing without you for three weeks, which is damned inconvenient. It'll only be worth it if you bring home a story which is guaranteed to boost our circulation. I'll give you another hint. The whisper is that no one comes across the kind of money Halliday has by being completely honest. See what you can discover.'

'He's hardly likely to tell me about anything like that!'

'You never know what he might let slip once you get

him talking. We'd have to check it thoroughly, of course, if you do come up with anything. We can't afford a libel action.'

'I didn't think *Citymag* was supposed to be a scandal-sheet!'

Wearily, Rudy said, 'It's called exposé reporting, dear. I want an in-depth interview, and if we find anything naughty in the bloke's past, I want to tell my readers about it—they're entitled to know how the man made his money. Some of it came from them.'

Cass chewed briefly on her underlip. 'Well, I'll keep my eyes and ears open. But I wish you'd tell me how you expect me to get this interview, let alone dig into the man's murky past.'

Rudy rolled his eyes heavenwards. 'Do I have to spell it out for you, girl? You're a woman, aren't you? And a good-looking one, at that. That tawny blonde hair of yours is quite arresting in sunlight—there should be plenty of *that* about in the tropics. Most men find the combination of green eyes and blonde hair pretty potent. You've got a nice little figure and good teeth, and—I thought—a modicum of intelligence. Smile at the man, for heaven's sake! He's not immune. He was married once, and his wife divorced him for fooling about with a dancer from some TV show. For a virtual recluse, he manages to have quite a time with the girls, I hear.'

Slightly unnerved by all this, Cass said, with faint indignation, 'You're not suggesting I should—should—use my——'

Rudy looked at her blandly. '—brain, dear girl. Use your brain—and anything else that your *brain* tells you might secure you an interview. You're not stupid—I hope. Play it by ear, but bring home the bacon, there's a good girl!'

Well, she would, if it was possible, Cass told herself, as she undressed for bed on board the *Princess*. She would use her brains—and she would smile at the man if it seemed necessary. But as for going any further than that—well, as Rudy had suggested, she would play it by ear. The first thing to do was track down her quarry.

That turned out to be anything but simple. There were nearly eight hundred passengers on board the *Princess*. And her preliminary enquiry at the purser's office drew a blank. No Lionel Halliday was listed among the eight hundred.

At first she was vastly relieved. It wasn't her fault if Rudy's information had been false. She could relax and enjoy her holiday and just not worry about it until she got home. Rudy would be furious, of course, but he couldn't blame her.

She spent the rest of the day with Lois, finding their way about the ship, and making friends with some of the other passengers. They were relaxing in striped deckchairs on the sundeck when she found the young man she had met at the foot of the stairs last night was standing close by, looking down at her.

'Hello,' he said, giving her a tentative grin.

Cass smiled back and, apparently needing no further invitation, he dropped into a chair beside her. 'We didn't get round to names last night,' he said. 'Mine is Trevor Wallace.'

Cass introduced herself and Lois, watching with secret amusement as Lois's dark eyes lit with eager interest. Trevor was a good-looking boy, and she supposed most girls would find him attractive. She guessed he would be about her own age, but her boy-friends had always been a few years older. She didn't mind at all that his initial interest in herself looked like being quite rapidly transferred to her cabin-mate.

She had virtually retired from the conversation, allowing the other two to talk across her, when Lois said, 'I'm trying to spot the celebrities! I think I saw one of the stars of my favourite Australian TV programme this morning.'

'*Are* there celebrities on board?' Trevor asked sceptically.

'Oh, there are bound to be at least one or two,' Lois said knowledgeably. 'But most of them travel incognito, of course.'

Cass smiled, wondering if Lois was romancing a little. Possibly she watched a little too much television, and gleaned her ideas on cruise ships from that quarter. Then the smile faded as Lois went on to say, 'It's the only way they can travel, if they don't want everyone to know just who they are. They often use another name.'

'But that's not as easy as it sounds,' Trevor objected, as Cass drew in a deep, apprehensive breath. 'It must be illegal, surely——'

'Not necessarily. There are all kinds of things you can do if you've got money and know-how.'

Yes, Cass thought. Of course there were. And who would have money and know-how, if not millionaires— one millionaire in particular.

It was one thing to go home without the interview that Rudy had demanded, if Lionel Halliday wasn't on the ship at all. But she had a strong feeling that he would think she had made a very poor showing if the man was on board using an alias. Rudy would no doubt expect her to ferret it out, regardless, and procure the interview by hook or by crook.

'Use your brains,' Rudy had told her. And he had been pretty certain of his facts. He wouldn't have let her come if he had not been sure that Halliday was on the ship.

Almost groaning aloud, she excused herself and left the other two chatting happily. She passed the bikini-clad sun-lovers stretched on the loungers about the pool and went to look over the stern railing. Watching the furling of the white wake behind the ship, she tried to think.

The only photographs of Lionel Halliday that Rudy had been able to give her were a photo-copy of a school cricket team photo, taken when he was in his teens, a newspaper cutting with a grainy picture of a man whose head was half turned from the camera as he spoke to another person, and one cut from a company brochure, in which Rudy had ringed one of a group of men sitting solemnly round a board table, but the man was partly obscured by the head of his neighbour at the table, and he had his own head lowered as he looked at a sheaf of papers in front of him. She wasn't sure that she would recognise Halliday from any of those.

She had a description, of course—dark brown hair, grey eyes, just touching six feet in height, average build. *Whatever that means*, she thought despairingly. Not fat nor extremely thin, she supposed.

It wasn't much to go on. He sounded like the perfect description of the 'average man'.

She wasn't even sure he would be travelling alone. Rudy hadn't known, and had hinted that he might have a 'travelling companion' along. Female, of course, was the unspoken implication. Rudy had thought it might complicate matters a little, but he was sure, he said, that Cass would get over any little difficulties.

She had a little more than two weeks. Might as well get started, she told herself resignedly. Eight hundred get started, she told herself resignedly. Eight hundred passengers, some of them women and children. She could rule out those, she supposed, unless it turned out that the elusive Mr Halliday was a master of disguise.

At least she knew his age—about thirty. So that would narrow the field a bit further. She needn't look at any man obviously over forty or under twenty-five. Even if he didn't look his age, that should leave a wide enough margin, surely. There couldn't be so very many men aboard who fitted the description. She would mentally sift and sort them and eventually, by a process of elimination and judicious deduction, would identify the right one.

She wandered along the promenade deck, trying to look casual as she studied the lounging figures in the deckchairs, and the few people hanging fascinatedly over the rail to watch the sea, almost glass-smooth and without whitecaps, although a gentle swell was visible as the ship nosed its way through the water.

One couple were consulting the newsletter that had been delivered to the cabins that morning, listing the activities available that day. That's an idea, Cass thought, and drew her own folded copy out from her canvas shoulder bag. What would interest a millionaire travelling incognito? There were any number of things to do, she discovered. Deck quoits, of course, and a deck tennis tournament; swimming—he probably had a pool of his own, back home, he just might be a swimmer. But the weather was still a little cool, and few people were braving the ship's pools today.

There were the lounges, each with its own bar. If he was a drinking man, he might be sitting imbibing in one of those. There were card rooms, but a peep into one of these showed most of the participants to be earnest and elderly. There was a floral arranging class being held in the Pacific Lounge, but she didn't think a property magnate would be terribly interested in that.

But—her heart suddenly beat faster with brief excitement. There was a lecture on finance and investment taking place right now in the theatre. *That* would be right up his street, wouldn't it? She stuffed the newsletter hastily into her bag and consulted the small plan of the ship thoughtfully provided by P & O.

Thirty minutes later, she emerged from the theatre feeling glassy-eyed with boredom and frustration. None of those at the lecture had remotely resembled the description of Lionel Halliday, and she had not dared to insult the lecturer by walking out, after arriving late and having him courteously wait for her to seat herself in the front row before resuming his talk.

Feeling a need for fresh air, she went up the forward stairs to the promenade deck, and stood at the rail. There was a window blocking access to the bow, and she glanced in and saw that some of the passengers were seated at tables, playing Scrabble or chess. She looked away, watching the restless, moving sea, stretching away to the boundless sky, and when her eyes grew tired she returned her gaze to the people through the window. A young couple laughing over their Scrabble board, a group of older people chatting as one of their number totted up a score, a family still engaged in their game—and two men hunched over a chessboard.

One of them had his back to her, and she could see an incipient bald patch in hair of an indeterminate, greying sandy colour as he contemplated his move. The other man was concentrating on the game, too, but he moved in his chair as she watched, and leaned back a little, smiling. He looked about thirty, his hair was dark brown and thick, straight and properly cut so that it lay close to his head, but was neither too long nor too short. He wore casual mustard-coloured slacks and a tan shirt that looked good on him, and expensive. As though he felt her suddenly concentrated gaze, he looked up directly into her eyes, and she saw that his were a cool, appraising grey.

Quickly, she moved away from the window, as though afraid that he could read her mind. *Could* it be him? He didn't look like the photographs, exactly, there was no instant recognition, but she couldn't say definitely that he could not be the man in the photographs, either. He had no hooked nose or widow's peak or missing tooth, to disqualify him. The man of the photographs looked ordinary—nondescript, but photographs could not show the penetration of grey eyes, the slight quirk of a mouth poised on the brink of a smile. The camera sometimes revealed personality, but in Lionel Halliday's case seemed to kill it altogether. The photographs might have been of anyone.

She had to get a better look at the man, of course. There was no doubt he was the first passenger who had answered to Lionel Halliday's description. She ought to somehow engineer an introduction. Time was so short.

She leaned against the rail, and turned with faked nonchalance to glance in the window again. The game must be over; the two men were standing up and making for the door. She mustn't let him just disappear—it might be ages before she found him again. She stepped quickly towards the door leading into the enclosed part of the ship, and opened her bag, rummaging in it with her head down as she walked towards the forward bar and the doorway to the side room which the two men were just leaving. She saw them coming towards her and, pretending to be engrossed in the contents of her bag, watched the two pairs of feet, and changed her course so that they could not avoid her. When the inevitable collision came, she lowered her shoulder so that the strap of the bag slid down her arm, at the same time tipping the opened bag before she allowed it to drop on to the carpet.

The result was chaos, of course. Her passport, notebook, folders of tickets, a small pack of paper handkerchiefs, strewed themselves over the floor. A lipstick rolled and was stepped on by one of the men. She heard the crunch as the plastic case splintered. Her sharpened pencil rolled too, and she saw one of the men stoop and pick it up. The other one had a firm hold on her elbow, steadying her. She looked up into grey eyes that held amusement as well as a faint surprise. She began to babble, her embarrassment not entirely false, since it wasn't a habit of hers to stage incidents in order to make men notice her. 'I'm terribly sorry! It was my fault, I wasn't looking——'

'You don't say!' the man murmured, and held her arm a few seconds longer before he stooped and began courteously to pick up her scattered belongings.

Her pencil was held out to her, along with the notebook, and she turned to the other man, smiling automatically as she thanked him. He didn't smile back, but gave a little bob of his head in acknowledgement. He had a moustache, darker than his nondescript hair, and quite bushy so that his mouth was half hidden in it. His pale eyes looked at her only fleetingly, with curiosity, and then he bent again to retrieve her passport for her. His companion was stuffing things back into the bag, but when he finished and stood up he held the ruined lipstick in one hand, regarding it ruefully as she took the bag from him. 'Sorry about that,' he said. 'I think I stepped on it.'

'It doesn't matter,' she assured him, trying out her most forgiving smile. 'I'm sure one of the shops on board can sell me another lipstick.'

The other man muttered something and walked away, and Cass, afraid that her quarry would follow suit, stood her ground in front of him with the smile fixed to her face. She held out her hand and he dropped the lipstick into it, and she replaced it in the bag and fastened the clasp.

'Let me buy you a drink,' he suggested, 'to make up for it.'

'Thank you,' she replied, thinking, Heavens! I thought you'd never ask! 'But there's really no need. It was my own fault, entirely.'

He took her arm again to lead her to one of the comfortable sofas in the bar. 'Oh, but there's every need,' he said, his quiet voice laced with faint mockery. 'It isn't every day that a pretty girl—er—throws herself in my way.'

She cast a quick glance at him as he seated himself beside her, her cheeks warming as she wondered if he meant that he was well aware their collision had not been accidental. But he was looking away from her, attracting the attention of one of the waiters. When he turned to her again, there was nothing but courteous enquiry in his voice as he asked what she would like.

She said, 'Gin and tonic, please,' and then sat looking at her clasped hands, trying desperately to think of something to say that wouldn't give away her anxiety to know who he was.

He spoke first. 'What's your name?'

'Cass,' she said, briefly meeting his eyes. 'Cass Reynolds. What's yours?'

She almost held her breath, although she knew that of course he wasn't going to say he was Lionel Halliday, even if he was. She raised her eyes again, wondering if she could tell if he was lying, and noticed that he hesitated just a fraction of a second before he said, 'Lucien Hale.'

CHAPTER TWO

Cass smiled at him, said, 'Hello, Lucien Hale,' and her mind said, *Lionel Halliday—Lucien Hale. The same initials of course.*

The grey eyes narrowed a little, and then he smiled back, a bland, charming smile, and his eyes dropped over her in a bold, masculine glance before he said softly, 'Hello, Cass,' and held her eyes with his.

Their drinks came, and she took hers rather thankfully, wondering if she had seemed over-eager. She had never needed to chase a man in her life, and it was humiliating if he thought that was what she was doing, now. She *had* literally thrown herself in his way, and she supposed he couldn't be blamed if he drew the obvious conclusion. If he *was* the millionaire, he was probably used to it, in spite of his previous disclaimer. No doubt her little ploy had been used before. She sighed inwardly. She had thought it was so clever, for a spur-of-the-moment scheme. The problem was how to keep things friendly without being too forthcoming.

He lifted his glass to her, saying, 'Here's to an enjoyable voyage.'

Her smile this time was a little strained, and she sipped her drink in silence.

'Are you travelling alone?' he asked her.

'Yes.' She told him about her aunt, sure this was a safe topic. 'And you?' she asked. 'Are you taking a well-earned break from business worries?'

'Do I look like a businessman?' he asked her, the amusement back in his eyes.

23

'Does that mean you're not?' she countered.

He smiled. 'I suppose nearly everyone is in business—of one sort or another.'

He was being deliberately enigmatic, but before she could challenge him, he said, 'And you—let me guess. You're—a model. Or an actress.'

She laughed. 'Nothing of the sort. I'm—I work in an office, actually.'

'Shorthand and typing?' he looked sceptical.

'Yes,' she said, without hesitation. She could do both, and often used them to take notes and compose her copy. But he would think she was a secretary. If he knew she was a journalist, at this stage, it might scare him off. Not that he looked easily scared. One might glance over him in a crowd, but close up there was a strength about his jaw, and a firmness in the line of his mouth, not to mention the unmistakably sharp intelligence that lurked behind the keen grey gaze. It crossed her mind that it might be better to own up to her true profession rather than have to confess later that she had deceived him, but he was speaking again, asking her if she had ever been on a cruise ship before. He seemed more relaxed now, his eyes lazily appreciative as they watched her, his arm going along the back of the couch as he leaned against the corner.

'This is my first time, ever, on a ship,' she told him. 'Have you cruised before?'

'A couple of times,' he said. 'It's a good way to unwind.'

She carefully kept her eyes fixed on the glass in her hand. The clues were mounting. Surely he *must* be Halliday. Hadn't Halliday's doctor recommended the cruise as a rest cure?

He started telling her about his other voyages, and she listened, forgetting for a time about her ulterior

motives and his probable identity. He had a way with
a story, keeping her interested and laughing until she
realised it was nearly dinner time.

'First sitting?' he queried, when she said she must
go and change.

'Yes. Aunt Claudine arranged it. She said it would
give me more time to take part in the shipboard activities, instead of spending the best part of the evening
eating. I know the seasoned travellers generally choose
the second sitting, though.'

He took her down to her cabin, and left her with a
casual word.

Lois had clothes scattered all over the cabin, trying
to decide what to wear. 'I told Trevor I'd go dancing
with him after dinner,' she said. 'I don't know whether
to wear my black satin trousers or this red skirt. Either
way, it'll have to be the white blouse. What do you
think, Cass?'

Cass thought Lois would look gorgeous in either,
she was a very pretty girl, but she pronounced in
favour of the skirt, and dressed herself in a cool natural
silk dress with a softly draped neckline and gently flar-
ing skirt, slipped her feet into bone-coloured high-
heeled sandals and fastened her hair back from her
temples with a tortoiseshell clasp.

After dinner, she declined to accompany Lois and
Trevor on their dance date, and instead went to the
evening cabaret that was performed for the passengers.
She chose a seat at the side of the big lounge, where
she could not only watch the performers, but could
also survey the audience.

There were only two or three men she could see
who might by any stretch of the imagination have met
the description of Lionel Halliday, and two of them
were obviously very much married with their families

along, while the third, she realised after a few minutes, was a member of the ship's crew.

The small troupe put on a professionally polished performance, and Cass applauded with the rest of the audience in the right places, but her mind was only half on the show. She hoped it was not going to be difficult to find again the man who called himself Lucien Hale.

In the event, she didn't even have to go looking. After the show she wandered through one of the bars on the way out, and he was just carrying a drink to a table, so that she almost bumped into him again.

He smiled, and said lightly, 'This is becoming a habit with you!'

Cass laughed and shook her head, and he caught at her elbow and said, 'Sit down. What'll you have to drink?'

After that it was easy. They sat in the bar for a while, and he said he had done all the talking that afternoon, and asked her about herself. She told him about her childhood and her family, and skirted around the subject of her job. Later they went to the disco where Trevor and Lois were energetically dancing, along with dozens of others, and for a short while they joined the throng on the floor.

Then they strolled on the promenade deck to the bows, where there was another small dance floor, and the band was playing. Here there were only a few couples taking advantage of the music, and the two of them danced into the small hours, until the band packed up and left a lone pianist playing soft background music. Cass had always loved dancing of any sort, and he was good, not flamboyant, but with a natural sense of rhythm, giving her a strong lead so that she followed him effortlessly. They talked very little, only smiling at each other now and then, and she forgot everything except the sense of sheer enjoyment of the present.

She refused his suggestion of a nightcap, and he took her down to her cabin. She fished her key out of the little bag she carried, and he suddenly put out a hand and took hers in it, preventing her from inserting the key in the lock. She took a quick little breath and looked up, and saw that his eyes were amused and knowing. His other hand came up behind her, at the waist, and pulled her firmly towards him, and then his mouth was on hers, warm and sure.

She stood quietly in his embrace, but her lips were unresponsive, and her body stiff. When he released her, he looked down at her with a questioning tilt to his brows. He had expected her to meet his kiss eagerly, and she had surprised him. Cass knew it, and wasn't sorry. She opened the hand that was fiercely clutching the key, and he took it from her and unlocked the door and pushed it open. As she turned to go in, he bent and planted a swift, light kiss on the curve of her neck and shoulder. She heard him say softly, 'Goodnight, Cass,' as she closed the door.

So he had kissed her goodnight, she told herself next morning. That was no big deal. Most women would have expected it. But she hadn't liked the way he had looked, just beforehand, as though he knew that *she* was waiting for it, almost as though he had decided to humour her. It rankled.

She was playing deck quoits with Lois and Trevor and one of Trevor's cabin-mates when she saw him standing on the sidelines watching them. He lifted his hand in greeting, so that she couldn't ignore him, and she sent him a brief smile and went on with the game.

He was still about when they finished, however, and she wasn't quite sure how, but he managed in the pleasantest way possible to whisk her away from the others, so that she found herself up on the sundeck, occupying a deckchair next to his.

She should have been pleased, she supposed, because he was definitely seeking her company this time, and that augured well for her plans. Rudy, if he had been here, would have told her to stop being an idiot and follow up her advantage. Instead, she felt constrained, by the knowledge that she was deceiving him, and by an uneasy feeling that her clumsy tactics had given him quite the wrong idea.

She didn't realise she was frowning until he put a gentle finger between her brows and queried, 'What's the matter?'

She shied away from his touch. 'Nothing.'

He looked at her keenly, then said, 'We dock at Noumea tomorrow. Are you going on one of the tours?'

She shook her head. 'I want to shop. I promised to buy perfume in Noumea for some of my friends.'

'Do you speak French?'

'No. Do you?'

'Some. Can I show you the town? I used to know it quite well.'

She stared at him, not quite believing her luck. He was smiling. He really liked her. Maybe when she knew him a little better, it wouldn't be difficult to get that interview. Surely he would forgive her the small deception at the beginning of their acquaintance?

'Thank you!' she said quickly. 'I'd like that very much.'

Noumea didn't look tropical, although the weather was warm. Cass was fascinated by the dress the native

Melanesian women wore, high-waisted 'Mother Hubbards' in colourful prints with frills of lace decorating the bodice and sleeves and the edge of the skirt, all styled in the same fashion but each one different by virtue of its pattern and lace decoration. The township was not very large, but there were innumerable small shops, and the tourists patronised the duty-free stores around the central square, with its old band rotunda surrounded by trees in blood-red bloom.

'The convicts used to put on concerts here, when the island was a penal colony,' Lucien told her. Cass called him Lucien, reminding herself she must temporarily try to forget that he more than likely had another name. A slip of the tongue on her part might be disastrous.

He translated for her in the shops, and proved to be quite knowledgeable about perfumes, a circumstance which she found oddly disturbing. They strolled about the market for a while, and Cass enjoyed herself in the boutiques of Le Village, with its old-world atmosphere of cobbled courtyard and colonial architecture. She had meant to return to the ship for lunch, but instead Lucien insisted on giving her a French meal. She wasn't game to try frog legs or snails, but settled for seafood and crisp fresh bread instead.

'That was delicious,' she told him afterwards, as they went back into the street. 'Thank you.' She stopped at a shop window to admire some carved Melanesian masks and strings of shell necklaces, and he asked, 'Fancy them?'

'No, not to keep. They're fascinating to look at, though, aren't they?'

'Yes, masks are an interesting concept.'

Cass looked at him enquiringly, and he continued, 'They're almost universal. Think of the ancient Greeks and their plays. All the players wore masks expressing their dominant characteristics. And most so-called primitive peoples seem to use either masks or face-paint in their rituals and dances.'

'Do they? I've never thought about it.'

'Not done any reading on the history of drama?' he enquired.

'I'm afraid not. An area of my education that's been sadly neglected, I suppose. Are you interested in drama?' She looked at him curiously, to find his answering look rather puzzling. He was regarding her with rather cool enquiry, and there was a moment's silence before he spoke.

'I've done some reading on the subject,' he said, 'but I suppose you're more familiar with the modern world of films.'

'Yes. Does that seem a philistine taste, to you?'

'Heaven forbid! Did I sound like an intellectual snob?'

'No.' She laughed up at him. 'Just frightfully know-ledgeable. Rather surprising, in a businessman.'

'Why? Even businessmen have other interests, surely. As a matter of fact, I'm very interested in films. Film and television are the cultural equivalent of the African tribal dances, a universally accepted medium of communication and—what's more important—of interpretation as well.'

'Interpretation?'

'Of life and death—and all the mysteries associated with them.'

'Yes, I suppose so. I've never really analysed it like that. I look on films as purely for entertainment, I suppose.'

'Have you never thought of acting as a career?' he asked her.

'Well, of course it is, for professionals——'

'No, I meant for yourself.'

'Good heavens, no! I mean—yes, when I was about twelve! Most girls think of it at some stage, like air hostessing, you know—the glamour image. But I don't have any such ambition, now. Nor, I'm afraid, the talent for it,' she added, wryly recalling the way she had manufactured their meeting.

'Don't you?' She heard the amusement in his voice, and turned away to hide the heat in her cheeks. His hand at her waist startled her, pulling her close to his side as they walked on. She stiffened a little, but he took no notice, and she yielded to his hold.

The ship sailed at four in the afternoon and Cass was on deck with Lucien to watch the shoreline recede. They leaned on the rail, with his hand imprisoning hers, the fingers strong and gentle at the same time. It felt very pleasant, and it troubled her.

'What are you doing tomorrow?' he asked her.

'We'll be at Vila,' she said.

'Yes. Spend the day with me?' His hand tightened slightly on her fingers.

'All right.' What else could she say? There was no reason to refuse, and every reason to accept. She knew he was watching her face, but she wouldn't look at him, afraid of seeing that knowing amusement again in his eyes. She supposed she had given him cause, but— a stirring of anger born of humiliation made her withdraw her hand from his. She said coolly, 'I have to go down to the cabin. I'll see you later.'

She was gone before he could detain her.

Lois was not there, and not for the first time, Cass unzipped the pocket inside her canvas shoulder bag and examined the three photographs she carried there. The schoolboy in the team photograph was giving a meaningless 'Say cheese' sort of smile, showing slightly prominent teeth. He'd have had them straightened, of course, and that would alter his appearance. In the second picture he was not smiling, but speaking to someone standing beside him, and the third was equally unhelpful, with no particular feature to link the man in the photographs with the man who called himself Lucien Hale. But equally there was nothing to disqualify him. Cass sighed, and put the pictures away as Lois came breezing into the cabin.

'Hey!' Lois exclaimed as she began shedding clothes and pulling more out of the wardrobe. 'Guess what? There's a millionaire on board!'

Cass tensed. 'How do you know?'

'We've been talking to one of the crew. Don't tell anyone, it's supposed to be dead confidential. But he swears it's true.'

'Did he say who?'

'No.' Lois shook her head regretfully. 'He said he's quite young, and he's got one of the suites on the main deck. They're awfully exclusive, you know, there are only four. There's a film producer in one of the others, and remember that TV star I told you I'd seen? Well, I *did*! It's her, all right. Wonder if she's travelling with the producer . . .'

'Lois, what do you do for a living?' queried Cass.

'I sell dresses in a department store in Melbourne. Why?'

'You've missed your vocation. You'd make a great columnist for one of those magazines for the star-struck. You know, who was seen wining and dining with whom, last.'

'Mm, wouldn't I, just? Now, what else do I know? There's a man who owns racehorses—are you interested in racing? And a bloke with a big sheep farm—I mean *big*, you know? But he's about fifty and fat with it. And an ex-opera singer, she's retired now, has been for years, but I believe she was quite famous, once upon a time. Do you want the bathroom?'

'Not just now, thanks,' Cass answered, laughing. 'You have it.'

'Thanks, love. I must say, you're a super cabin-mate.' About to close the bathroom door, Lois turned and said, 'Have a good day? You went out with that rather dishy feller, didn't you?'

'Very nice, thanks.'

Lois hesitated, as though waiting for something more, then grinned and went into the bathroom.

After dinner Cass went with Lois and Trevor and two of his young friends to the disco. She had been dancing energetically with one of the men and was about to sit down when a detaining hand caught at her wrist, and Lucien's voice said in her ear, 'Dance with me.'

Most of the couples on the floor were dancing apart from each other, but he put both hands on her waist and kept her close as he moved to the rhythm of the music. After a few minutes, he said softly, 'Why did you run away this afternoon?'

'I didn't run away. I just had things to do, that's all.'

'Such as?'

She threw back her head and looked at him. 'What gives you the right to put me through a third degree?'

His answering look was steady and curious. 'I *thought* you were annoyed with me,' he said. 'Why? If you didn't want to spend the day with me tomorrow, you only had to say no.'

'I wasn't annoyed with you,' she lied. 'You're imagining things.'

A small frown drove between his brows for a moment, then he smiled. 'Okay, if you say so.'

They stayed with the crowd for the remainder of the evening, and he didn't monopolise her; she danced with the other men at the table, and he asked Lois to dance, and later asked another woman who was sitting at another table, alone, for a dance. Cass went down to the cabin with Lois after midnight, making it clear that she neither wanted nor needed an escort.

Vila, the capital of Vanuatu, slid into view early the following morning, set in a tropical backdrop of thickly growing palms, a picture-postcard place. The town seemed a prosperous commercial centre, and Cass was delighted with the batik printed clothes shown in the shops, and the beautiful embroidered blouses. She bought several, finding the prices very reasonable, before they climbed aboard a mini-bus which drove them into the countryside and through copra planta-tions lining the road, to a strip of sand where they awaited transportation to a tiny islet only a few hundred yards offshore.

It was called Hideaway Island, and a small group of tourists were ferried to it in a flat-bottomed boat by a romantically garbed island boatman, a flower-pat-terned *sulu* about his hips, and a wreath of hibiscus and spiky palm leaves atop his black curls.

They swam in the warm, calm tropical waters of the lagoon, and as she floated on her back, watching the tall palm fronds swaying gently against a cobalt sky, Cass couldn't help laughing a little at the blissful re-semblance to a travel agent's poster.

Lucien surfaced beside her, shaking water from his darkened hair. 'What's the joke?' he demanded.

She made to stand up, and found the coral with

which the sea-bed and beach were strewn was sharp on the feet. 'Ouch!' she exclaimed, and laughed again. 'I was just thinking it's too idyllic for words, but this coral isn't. It should be all soft white sand, to complete the picture!'

'Even Eden had its serpent,' he reminded her, as she turned over and began swimming slowly to the shore. 'There is some sand, though. We'll find it, later.'

They lunched on fish baked in leaves, taro, and fried tapioca chips, curried chicken and roasted pork, fluffy white rice, and delicious salads including coconut and papaws, all served in the open and eaten at tables shaded by a thatched roof supported by stout poles, overlooking the lagoon. A small band entertained them while they ate, singing a mixture of pop songs and island melodies, and after lunch there was the opportunity to explore part of the reef in a glass-bottomed boat.

Cass watched spellbound as the litter of dead white coral shapes gave place to great canyons and mountain slops of the stuff, with blue and yellow outcrops of living coral growing on them. Tiny electric-blue fish darted about in shoals, and bigger butter-yellow ones undulated about lazily. A huge spotted sea-slug appeared, and a couple of zebra-striped fish hid behind a flower-like coral growth. They passed over a canyon so deep that the water became murky and deeply green, falling away, it seemed, for miles below them, and as Cass exclaimed in excited fear, Lucien put his hand over hers and held it tightly.

Afterwards, they explored the little island on foot, following narrow paths through a tangle of tropical growth studded with red, white and purple blooms. At the other side of the island they found sand and a banyan tree, and a view of the mainland shore across the calm water. Somewhere a bird called, and Cass lifted her head, turning to identify the bird. Lucien was closer than she expected, and his hand came about her waist and pulled her to him, and he kissed her, finding her mouth with devastating accuracy.

She found herself responding to the kiss before she had time to think about it. His mouth was warmly insistent, and as he drew her closer to him, she felt the beating of his heart against his breast, and the heat of his thighs burning through her flimsy cotton skirt. His hand was roaming up and down her back, bringing soft shivers of excitement, and when he lifted his mouth at last, he pressed it to her neck and then her bare shoulder, and said quietly, 'Let's sit on the sand, now we've found it.'

She didn't have a chance to answer him, because a family party came round a bend in the path, and she started and pushed away from him, turning to stare blindly at the farther shore. Two children ran squealing on to the sand and splashed into the shallow water at its edge, followed by their parents, and Lucien sighed and said ruefully, 'Well, perhaps not. This island is overpopulated for its size.'

Cass laughed, and the slight tension eased. He took her hand and they walked on, soon finding themselves back at the thatched shelter, among the other tourists. They watched one of the islanders split fresh coconuts expertly with a huge curved machete, and sampled the sweet white flesh, and inspected the colourful clothing sold in the small shop nearby, and then it was time to return to the township and the port.

Cass slipped away from him with the excuse of needing a shower and a change before dinner, but the ship didn't sail until late in the evening, and he found her some time after dinner, leaning over the rail of the promenade deck, listening to the music of a band that was playing on the wharf.

'Come on down,' he suggested. 'We've a good hour or so before we have to be back on board.' And they went out into the tropical dusk, listened to the music, and strolled along the wharf, inspecting the shells and beadwork, woven basketware and carvings, and the colourful leis and grass skirts and printed cotton dresses and shirts laid out on mats, and lit by the ship's lights. Cass admired a trumpet-shaped shell, spiky at the edge, and smoothly pink inside, and Lucien bought it for her, stilling her protest with a curt, 'Don't be silly. It's only a couple of dollars. It's hardly a mink.'

She laughed then, and thanked him, and mischievously bought a gaudy lei of shiny paper and dropped it about his neck. His smile was sardonic, she knew he wasn't the type for the usual tourist gimmicks, and that he was well aware she was teasing him. But he didn't take the garland off. Only there was a glint behind the smile in his eyes that made her suddenly slightly nervous of him.

When the ship slid away from the port, they were standing up on the darkened sundeck, and as they picked up speed and she shivered in the freshening breeze, Lucien's arm came about her and pulled her into a secluded corner. She was reluctant, aware that this was the stuff of the famed 'shipboard romance', a sort of filmic and literary cliché which she really didn't want to be part of. Warring thoughts and emotions chased each other about her mind. He was very attractive and she liked him, but she hated the thought of being looked on as an easy conquest, a passing diversion; she had only known him for a few days, and she had never given kisses casually. On the other hand, she

couldn't forget that her job might depend on his con-
tinuing to like her.

Confused, she went unresistingly into his arms as he
drew her to him, but her lips were unresponsive, and
after a few moments he lifted his mouth from hers and
rubbed his chin against her temple, saying softly,
'What's the matter?'

She was silent for a moment, wondering how much
she could say. Finally, she said, 'It's all—so unreal,
somehow. Romance in the tropical moonlight. I—find
it hard to believe in.'

Lucien laughed a little, and she felt his breath against
her forehead. 'You feel real enough to me,' he said,
and his hand moved caressingly over her hip and up to
cup her breast firmly. 'And I think I can prove to you
that *I'm* real.'

She tried to say, 'Don't!' but his mouth silenced her,
with a blatant sensuality that was not the stuff of
dreams, but of an earthy, inescapable reality. His hand
was still on her breast, moving gently, arousing sensa-
tions she hadn't, until then, known about. And when
she tried to repulse it with her own hand, he grabbed
her fingers and pushed them inside the opening of his
shirt, holding her palm against the warm, hard wall of
his chest. She curled her fingers instinctively, her nails
scraping against his skin, and felt him give a tiny
shudder and heard a deep, soft moan in his throat.
Knowing she had inadvertently fed his desire, she felt
an unexpected surge of answering passion, mingled
with triumph, and as his lips determinedly parted hers,
her body suddenly became fluid and responsive, her
mouth soft and submissive to his.

He kissed her for a long time, and when he stopped
she was glad he was still holding her closely, because
her legs wouldn't have held her. His breathing was a

little harsh as he said, 'Well—satisfied?'

Her body was far from satisfied, it was crying out desperately for some kind of fulfilment, for the natural end to the raging desire he had awakened, that she told herself fiercely she must somehow control.

His lips brushed her earlobe, and settled in the small hollow beneath it, as he muttered, 'I'm real, Cass, and I really want you. You share your cabin, don't you?'

'Yes,' she whispered.

'I don't.' He let that sink in. 'Cass?' His hand cupped her head, and he kissed her again, softly, and said against her mouth, 'Come down there with me. I want to make love to you.'

It was an effort, but she managed to move her mouth away from his, and, trying to pull out of his arms, she said, 'I can't.'

'Can't? You mean you can't, tonight?'

'No, I—oh, please let me go!' she said. She couldn't think with his arms about her like this, with the warmth and strength of him so close.

His hold slackened, but he still held her. 'You want to, don't you?' he asked her bluntly.

Her face flamed painfully in the darkness. 'No!' she said. 'I hardly know you!'

Lucien laughed. 'That didn't seem to matter a few minutes ago.'

'Yes, well——' she muttered shamefacedly. 'You're pretty experienced, aren't you? Maybe you're used to taking girls to bed on a couple of days' acquaintance, but I'm not—I mean, I don't usually——'

As she floundered, he said calmly, 'Are you trying to tell me that you're not that sort of girl?'

Almost wincing at the trite expression, but unable to come up with a better one, Cass said resignedly, 'Yes, I suppose that *is* what I'm trying to say. It's much too soon, and—well, I didn't mean to give you the wrong impression. I'm sorry.'

'You got carried away by the tropical moon, is that it?'

'*You* had rather a lot to do with it, too,' she confessed honestly. 'You're actually pretty potent—I suppose you know.'

'It's nice to be told,' he said, quite gravely. 'Thank you.'

He was still holding her, and she made an experimental move, found it was still impossible to escape, and begged, 'Please, Lucien, let me go.'

'In a moment,' he said. He seemed to be trying to see her face in the darkness. 'Tell me, how long should an acquaintanceship be, do you think, before it's—er—permissible—to make love to a girl who "isn't that sort"?'

He would probably think it terribly funny and naïve if she mentioned a wedding ring, she supposed. One didn't confess impossible ideals to people who treated sex so casually. Besides, caution intervened when she remembered her assignment. Her conscience pricked her, but pragmatism said, Don't give too much away. She remembered Rudy saying impatiently, Use your brain, girl—and anything else that your brain tells you might be useful.

She said, 'I can't answer that. It depends, doesn't it, on—on circumstances and the people concerned.'

'Does it?' Lucien released her at last. 'You'd better run along to bed, little girl.'

'Don't patronise me!' she flashed, suddenly angry. 'Just because I don't share your alley-cat morals!'

There was a tense silence. She wanted to get away from him, but he blocked the way, big and suddenly menacing. When he spoke his voice was chilly. 'I'm sorry,' he said, moving pointedly out of the way. 'I'll try not to contaminate your chaste person again.'

She didn't go immediately, and he added rather savagely, 'If you don't *move* pretty quickly, I'll be tempted to find out just how impregnable that vaunted virtue of yours really is!'

She went then, her throat raw with anger and humiliation, and hot tears pricking at her eyes. He was hateful, it had all been nothing but sex and moonlight, and she was very glad that she had had enough sense to stop him before it was too late. She didn't even care at the moment about the wretched interview. Rudy might expect her to go to any lengths to get a story, but there were certain things she had to draw the line at.

It was some time later, as she lay gazing into the darkness in the cabin, and listening to the insistent slap and swish of the water against the hull, that she admitted to herself that the story had had nothing whatever to do with her response to the man, or with the urgent, shaming temptation to accept his invitation to go to his cabin. She wasn't sure whether that made it worse or better.

CHAPTER THREE

THEY had two days at sea before they arrived at Suva. The water changed from a smooth-surfaced blue to a patchwork of white-capped waves, and the ship began to pitch as it ploughed its way onward. The doctor's surgery was filled with people suffering from sea-sickness, and Lois spent most of her time lying back in one of the deck chairs on the promenade deck and trying not to think about her stomach. Cass kept her company out of sympathy, but she knew her own sense of misery was caused less by the motion of the ship than by the sharp words she had exchanged with Lucien, and the fact that he no longer seemed inter-ested in knowing her. She had seen him once or twice on deck, and he had nodded distantly and turned away, making her feel snubbed, and once when Cass and Trevor had persuaded Lois to venture into one of the bars for a drink of lemonade, Lucien had been at a nearby table with his erstwhile chess opponent and a young blonde girl who exuded the kind of sulky sexua-lity which men were universally supposed to find irre-sistible.

Her gloom was increased by the certainty that no one else on board answered to the description of Lionel Halliday, and that Rudy was going to be livid when she arrived home and told him she had failed her assignment.

At Suva, she went ashore with a thankful Lois and several other young people who made up a lively party. They bargained for jewellery and carvings at the stalls along the waterside, bought native handicrafts at the special market nearby, and wandered, fascinated, about the food market where pineapples, bananas, yams, coconuts and all kinds of indigenous foodstuffs lay in open bins, and coloured wrapping paper hung above the stalls like rainbow decorations.

They walked to the shops past huge copra sheds, where the smell of coconut, sweet and heavy, permeated the air, and later they bought handprinted cotton dresses and shirts from the numerous small stores crammed from floor to ceiling with cheap, colourful clothing. Some of the group invested in transistor radios, calculators and portable tape-players, and Cass fell for the temptation of an Indian silver necklace worked in an intricate pattern.

She wore it that evening, when three busloads of passengers were taken along the foreshore for several miles to see the Fijian ritual of firewalking. She sat with Lois and Trevor, all of them eagerly expectant. The dancing troupe performed for them first, dressed in green leafy skirts and floral garlands, the women graceful and pretty and the men fierce in their wardances. The small cleared space was surrounded by tropical palms, and the grass where the dances were performed was shorn and neat, so that it looked very like a stage. The spectators sat under a thatched awning on tiers of seats, and behind the dancers a huge fire glowed and lit the performance, giving it a pagan splendour.

It was all very lighthearted, and the Fijian master of ceremonies explained that the firewalking in this case had no religious significance, but was done for the fun of it, and part of the preparation was the engendering of a happy mood on the walkers.

The women retired from the scene, and the men

leaped about the fire, singing and whooping, raking the piled logs away and leaving the stones exposed, glowing red hot. Flash bulbs kept an almost continuous flare of light on them as the men, at first one by one, and then two or three together, walked over the stones, smiling and sometimes posing for several seconds as their bare feet trod squarely on the heated stones. The audience was hushed, the tension tangible, at the beginning. Then as the walkers succeeded each other, applause began to ripple about the enclosure, along with laughter and murmurs of disbelief.

When it was all over, several of the men sat on the grass and presented their unharmed feet for inspection, grinning widely. More photos were taken, and the audience began to wander back to the buses.

Lois and Trevor shared a seat, and Cass found a place a little farther back, but the bus was filling rapidly, and when a man hesitated at the empty place beside her she looked up with a ready smile.

'May I?' Lucien asked, as the smile wavered a little with surprise and embarassment.

'Yes, of course,' she said, rather stiffly. She turned her head aside to gaze out of the window as he sat down and the driver started the engine.

There was no glass, only a rolled canvas which ran the length of the bus and was fastened with numerous straps. The night air combined with the speed of the bus as it roared along the coast road created a brisk breeze, and Cass shivered, huddling her arms around her.

'Here.' A light wool sweater was dropped about her shoulders, and she turned to Lucien in surprise.

'Thank you. But you——?'

'I'm okay.' He was wearing casual off-white slacks and an open-necked brown shirt, the sleeves rolled to the elbow. He didn't look cold, although the breeze was ruffling his hair, as it blew hers about her face.

She made to pull back the flying strands, and found that some of them had caught in the silver necklace. Lucien watched as she fiddled, trying to untangle it.

'Let me,' he said, and brushed her fingers aside. She felt his touch on her neck for long seconds, before he pushed her hair back, freed, and said, 'There. Better?'

'Thank you very much,' she said politely. Then, because there would never be a better chance, she said, 'Lucien, I'm sorry for what I said the other night—about your morals. I had no right to—well, jump to conclusions like that.'

He looked at her thoughtfully, and then gave a slightly rueful smile. 'That's a very handsome apology. I'm sorry, too, Cass.' His hand lifted and brushed her cheek. 'I was suffering from frustration, if it's any excuse, when I savaged you.'

'Well,' she said rather carefully, 'I guess—so was I.'

She wasn't looking at him, but he put a finger under her chin and raised her face, his eyes grave before he bent and gave her a featherlight kiss on her lips. Then he sat back a little, and his hand went to the necklace at her throat. 'Been shopping?'

'Yes. Do you like it?'

'Very much. It suits you. Did you enjoy the fire-walking?'

'I'm not sure if "enjoy" is the right word. It was fascinating, though. It isn't faked, is it?'

'Apparently not. The "experts" have come up with no explanations. A pure case of mind over matter, it seems.'

The journey back to the ship was a short one, but by the time the bus drew up on the wharf, the rather stilted conversation had given way to genuine ease with each other, as though their tentative friendship had never been broken.

Going up the gangway, Cass shrugged the sweater off and handed it to him, and Lucien invited, 'Come and have a nightcap with me?'

Lois, with a lift of her brows and an understanding smile, had gone ahead with Trevor. Cass hardly hesitated before she said, 'Yes, I'd like that.'

Later Lucien left her at her cabin door with a quick, light kiss on her temple, and a humorous quirk of his lips. As Cass closed the door behind her, Lois sat up in her bunk, where she had been lying reading, and asked, 'Everything okay, now?'

Cass smiled. 'I think so.' Lois had been very tactful, obviously curious but not breathing a word about the sudden coolness between Cass and Lucien.

'Oh, good. It's only a short cruise, after all,' said Lois. 'If you like him, it's a shame to waste time,' She put away her book and wriggled down under the blankets. 'We get to Savu Savu quite early in the morning,' she said. 'They say there's not much to do there except go to the hotel for a drink and a swim, or go native, whatever that means.'

Cass undressed slowly. It was true there was very little time. And she had wasted two whole days. Perhaps tomorrow she could make up for it.

Savu Savu was a small community in the north of the Fiji group. The ship anchored offshore, and the passengers were taken ashore in the motorised tenders. The hot tropical sun beat down on dark banana, breadfruit and palm trees, and reflected glaringly off the white road to the township. Scarlet poinsettias and scented white frangipani grew like weeds.

Lucien had found Cass after breakfast, and they went ashore together. They strolled along the road, stopping to admire the shells, necklaces, grass skirts and handicrafts that were being sold at temporary stalls along the way, and every so often sat on the grass beneath one of the scattered trees along the shoreline, to seek a respite from the sun.

Mop-headed dark children followed them, chattering happily in English, and offering to show them the Springs which were the major tourist attraction, albeit a fairly minor one. To Cass, who had seen Rotorua several times, the small steaming hole in the ground and the warm water running down to the ocean across the beach were interesting but hardly riveting.

Far more intriguing to her eyes was the small islet just across the bay, and the romantic-looking old wreck half-submerged at the edge of the golden sand that fringed the islet. One enterprising young Fijian offered to ferry them across, but his small outrigger was made of corrugated iron, only a few inches of which remained above water when he jumped into it, the better to entice them. Lucien looked down at her with a quizzical question in his eyes, noted the swift shake of her head, and firmly declined the offer.

After they had visited the local market, listened to an impassioned preacher on a street corner, (without, however, understanding a word), and enjoyed the harmonious sound of a few hymns sung by his followers, they made their leisurely way back to the wharf in time to reach the ship for lunch al fresco on the deck.

'If I can rustle up some reliable-looking transport,' said Lucien, 'would you like to go to the island this afternoon?'

Cass looked longingly at the sand-ringed little island with its mysterious, graceful palms, and her eyes went dreamy. 'It can't possibly be as perfect as it looks,' she sighed.

'Would you rather keep your romantic dreams than find out what the real thing is like?'

He sounded scoffing, and she looked at him and saw a challenge in the grey eyes. 'No,' she said. 'Let's see if we can find a boat to take us there.'

They did, and a boatman who promised to call for them in plenty of time before the ship sailed.

Lucien had a canvas bag holding their swimming things and towels, and as the boat made back to shore, he held out his hand to Cass and said, 'Well?'

She took his hand, and allowed him to lead her along the beach to the wreck. It had an air of quiet melancholy, and close up the sound of the water lapping in and out of the splintered and rotting timbers had an almost sinister note.

'Do you want to explore it?' he asked.

'No. It might not be safe.'

'True. Some things are best viewed from a distance.'

They climbed up the slope behind the beach, into the grove of coconut palms which virtually covered the island, and down the other side, where the only view was of the vast Pacific, blue and sparkling as a fairytale ocean. Cass stood on the white-gold sand, turned over a pink and white trumpet shell with her foot, breathed the soft air with its tang of sea and sunshine and a faint whiff of perfumed flowers and coconut, and said, 'I think I've somehow strayed into a travel poster. Pinch me, Lucien, I'm dreaming.'

'I'll do better than that.' Dropping the canvas bag on the sand, he took her shoulders in firm hands and kissed her.

It was a deeply satisfying kiss. His mouth was warm and expert and very persuasive, and she put her hands on his shoulders and kissed him back without reserve.

When he stopped, she looked into his eyes with a smile in hers, and said, 'I'm still dreaming.'

For a moment he looked as though he intended to do something about it, and Cass softly drew in her breath. Then his mouth quirked in a slightly grim smile, and his hands fell away from her.

He bent to open the bag, and took out his rolled towel. 'I want to swim,' he said. 'What about you?'

'Yes,' she said. Over her bikini she wore the *sulu* she had bought in Suva, and she untied the knot that held it and let the bright wrap fall to the sand. Lucien stripped to dark swim shorts that hugged his lean hips, then took her hand and they ran into the warm, welcoming water together.

Afterwards they spread their towels on the sand and lay soaking up the sun, letting it dry the salt water on their bodies. Cass closed her eyes, images of fringed palms dancing against her lids. She could hear the stiff leaves clacking slightly in the faint breeze that stirred them. Then a shadow fell across her, and Lucien's mouth touched hers, softly at first, then more firmly, as his hand began to stroke her shoulder and arm, and the bared skin between the bra and the tiny pants of her bikini.

His mouth lifted, and she opened her eyes and looked into his, darkened and smiling, with a lurking passion behind the smile. He murmured, 'You're not dreaming,' and kissed her again, coaxing her lips apart and caressing them with his tongue. His fingers brushed her thigh, then his body shifted over hers, his arm cradling her as her head was bent back under the increased pressure of his mouth.

Cass felt a sudden rush of wanton feeling, and her instinct was to press herself against him and pull him closer to her. She curbed it with an effort, and made a movement of denial instead, trying to wriggle away from him, pushing at his hand.

He raised his head and looked at her. 'I won't hurt you,' he said, his voice deep and lazy. 'Don't be scared of me.'

His hand went to her waist, holding her intimately, and he kissed her throat and shoulder, making her shiver with pleasure. He felt it, and slid both arms around her, bearing her down on the towel over the soft sand, and she saw the blaze of desire in his eyes. He bent to kiss her again, and she turned her head aside and gasped, 'No, Lucien—please don't!'

'Why not?' His mouth was against her skin, beneath her ear.

'Because—because I'm asking you!'

He moved again, looking down at her with mockery. 'Why?' he asked again. 'Don't you like it?'

Cass bit her lip, and then bravely met his eyes. 'You know very well I do,' she said. 'That's why—I want you to stop.'

A rueful smile lit his eyes. He held her for a moment longer, then rolled away on to his back. A breath of laughter escaped him. 'Oh, Cass,' he sighed, 'what a devastating weapon your total honesty is!'

'I'm sorry.'

'What for?' He raised himself on one elbow and looked at her. 'For wanting me—or for not wanting me enough?'

Cass sat up, looking away from him, her arms hugging her knees. That remark about her honesty troubled her. 'For—letting you go so far,' she said quietly, 'when I didn't mean to——'

She made a little gesture with her hand, and Lucien reached out and caught her fingers in his, sat up beside her and put her palm to his mouth, then nipped gently at her thumb with his teeth before he released her. 'Okay,' he said, 'I've got the message.'

She looked at him doubtfully, and he touched her cheek and said, 'Don't look so worried. Want to go for a walk?'

They wandered along the beach, finding broken shells and bits of coral, and paddling in and out of the shallows. He didn't seem angry, and she was grateful for that, because she supposed she had, to some extent, led him on.

They returned to the little beach and packed up their gear, and when the boatman called for them they were waiting. Lucien hired one of the island taxis to return them to the wharf and the tender, and as they climbed up the precarious-looking gangway slung down the side of the ship, he caught Cass's arm and said, 'There are no dinner reservations tonight. Will you have yours with me? I can get us a table for two.'

She was slightly surprised, but pleased. 'Yes,' she said, and smiled at him rather shyly as they stepped on board. 'That would be very nice.'

It was pleasant sitting at a small table with him, talking quietly about their day, about the other islands, and then animatedly discussing films they had seen and books they had read, finding that their tastes coincided in some areas, diverged in others.

Lucien said, as they sipped their coffee, 'Tomorrow is Island Night on board. Do you have a grass skirt?'

She smiled. 'No, I'll wear my *sulu*, I suppose. And maybe a flower in my hair. There's a morning class tomorrow—we're to learn how to make paper flowers and leis, and to dance an island dance.'

He smiled. 'Which side are you going to wear the flower on?'

'What do you mean?'

'Don't you know? If you wear it on the right side, you have a man. If you wear it on the left, you're—still looking. Wear it on the right, Cass.'

She looked at him, and saw that his eyes were dark and gentle. Her own gaze wavered away. He was merely playing, she told herself. He certainly wasn't in the least serious about her. Deliberately, she reminded herself of the girl he had been sitting with in the bar only a couple of days back.

She didn't wear a flower in her hair at all, only tied two on to her wrists with ribbon, and when Lucien saw her he raised his brows and smiled, his eyes teasing. 'Leaving your options open?' he murmured.

She didn't answer, and he took her arm to steer her into the big lounge where the ship's entertainment company put on a short concert of island songs and dances, before inviting the passengers to perform. Lois dragged Cass on to the floor, and with about thirty other women of all ages they performed the dance one of the crew had taught them that morning. Cass hadn't realised it was to be a competition, and was a little embarrassed when she found herself repeating the dance with half a dozen 'finalists'. In the end she was judged second, and returned to her seat beside Lucien clutching her prize—a box of chocolates and a diary and pencil with the ship's name embossed on them.

'Very nice,' commented Lucien. 'You're a girl with hidden talents, aren't you?'

'Oh, you don't know the half of it,' she said lightly, with a hollow feeling in her stomach. He certainly didn't, and she must find a way soon of disclosing to him who—or rather, *what*—she really was, and hope that he liked her enough to forgive her the small deception.

But this was hardly the time or the place. The compère was calling on all the men who had dressed the part for the Island Night to take the floor and perform a war-dance, and there was a great deal of noisy laughter, soon drowned by the music and the gruesome 'war-cries' resounding about the room.

They joined in the applause when it was over and the winner, a wizened little man who had removed his false teeth and won by virtue of the fearsome faces he made, had collected his prize.

'Shall we dance?' Lucien asked her, as the floor cleared and the band began to play a dreamy island tune.

Swaying in time to the music, with his arms about her and her hands resting against his chest, she forgot everything but the music and the moment. It was enough just to be here, like this, with him. When the band stopped for a rest, she moved away from him reluctantly and allowed him to lead her back to where they had been sitting.

The sulky-looking blonde girl was sitting there, gloomily swirling a drink in a large glass. She looked up as they approached, and smiled past Cass at Lucien. 'You don't mind, do you, darling? I'm so *bored* and lonely!'

Lucien said, 'Cass, this is Patsy. Patsy—Cass.'

Cass smiled stiffly and said, 'Hello, Patsy.'

Patsy gave her a comprehensive glance. 'Hi! I saw you doing that hula thing. You do look the part I must say.'

'Thanks,' said Cass, almost giggling at the studiedly patronising way the girl spoke. She obviously didn't think much of the *sulu*, which Cass had thought rather fetching. Patsy was dressed in a stunning red silk cheong-sam which Cass fancied she had seen earlier in the ship's boutique, and it certainly suited her, showing off a slim waist and nicely rounded hips and bust to perfection, while the side slit displayed a length of very shapely leg.

Patsy wriggled along on the banquette and patted the seat beside her invitingly, smiling at Lucien. But he made Cass sit down first, and seated himself beside her with his arm along the back of the seat behind her shoulders. 'Want a drink?' he asked as one of the waiters came near.

Cass shook her head. But Patsy downed the remainder of what was in her glass and said, 'I could do with another.'

Lucien ordered it for her, but it had not come when the band started to play again, and Patsy began ostentatiously to swing one black-sandalled foot in time to the beat, humming along with the tune.

'Do you mind?' Lucien murmured in Cass's ear, and leaned across her to ask Patsy if she wanted to dance.

Her smile transforming her face, the girl leaped up eagerly and preceded him on to the floor, where she promptly flung her arms about his neck and danced as though she was glued to him.

The drink came, and Cass stared at it fixedly, willing herself to look unconcerned. It didn't *matter*, for heaven's sake, if Patsy was attracted to Lucien. It didn't matter if the attraction was mutual. All that really matters to you, my girl, she told herself grimly, is that you get that interview before this cruise is over.

When they came back, Patsy was looking flushed, and giggling. Lucien, Cass thought as she glanced at his face, was regarding the other girl as though she was a slightly wayward but very engaging child. A smile tugged at the corner of his mouth, and his eyes, answering the blatant message in hers, were knowing and enigmatic.

With a rush of antagonism, Cass thought, we all amuse him, we women. He regards us as pretty playthings for his pleasure. He must be getting a mighty kick out of having the two of us competing for his favours.

Well, he wasn't going to have it all his own way, she decided. She could hardly get up and walk away, it would look like pique. Instead, she turned to Patsy, gave her a friendly smile and began asking her where she came from, and what she did for a living.

'I came from Mildura,' Patsy told her, 'but I live in Sydney, now. I'm a model.'

It was hard going at first. Patsy was patently of the opinion that talking to a member of her own sex was something of a waste of precious time. But Cass wasn't a journalist and a pretty darned good interviewer for nothing. And Patsy wasn't proof against the warm, flattering interest of her questions. Within five minutes she was beginning to tell Cass her life story, and in ten she had covered her childhood in Mildura and had reached the stage of her first exciting days in Sydney, going to modelling school at night and working behind a counter in the daytime to pay for her tuition. She went on to describe a recent modelling assignment in New Zealand, but Lucien touched Cass's shoulder and said, 'Dance?'

She rose with a show of reluctance, and when he took her in his arms she was not quite as pliant as before.

'I'm sorry about that,' he said, with slight movement of his head towards where Patsy still sat. 'She *is* lonely, poor kid, and I don't want to give her the brush-off.'

'Of course not!' Cass answered instantly. 'Why should you?'

'Because I wanted to spend the evening with you.'

'Well, now you have two of us to spend it with,' she said brightly.

'Look, we can go through to the other bar, if you'd rather——'

'Certainly not. I like talking to Patsy. She's led a very interesting life.'

'She hasn't even *got* to the interesting part, yet,' Lucien said rather dryly. 'I'm not sure if your innocent ears can stand it.'

'Oh, don't be silly!' she said crossly. 'I'm a——' she almost said *journalist*, and stopped herself just in time. 'I'm a big girl,' she amended quickly. 'I'm not so easily shocked.'

When they returned to their seats, Patsy was talking animatedly to a dark young man who was gazing at her with blatant admiration. 'This is Tony,' she said, without any further explanation, and Lucien waved to the young man to keep his seat, while he found an extra chair for himself.

At least it made the numbers even, Cass thought. Somehow they had become a foursome, but it was soon obvious that Patsy hoped to interest Tony in Cass, while she herself concentrated on Lucien. The situation at any other time would have been wildly funny, but somehow tonight she didn't feel like laughing. The fact that Lucien was evidently wickedly amused exacerbated her annoyance.

She saw Lois leaving at about eleven-thirty, looking a little pale, and excused herself to go over and ask if her cabin-mate was all right.

'I have been,' said Lois, 'but the darned boat is pitching again, and I'm beginning to feel rather woozy.

I'll be fine once I'm in bed.'

'Do you want me to come down with you?' Cass asked.

'No, of course not. You enjoy yourself. I'm okay, truly, just as long as I can lie down.'

'Well, if you're sure—I won't be very long, though. I'm not making a night of it.'

She saw Lois into the lift, and was turning to go back to the lounge when Lucien came up behind her and caught at her arm. 'This way,' he said, and steered her towards the stairs, going upward.

'Where are we going?' she demanded. 'What about Patsy and——'

'Patsy's got Tony,' he said. 'She doesn't need me!'

He sounded goaded, and Cass looked up at him as he almost pushed her out on to the darkened deck, seeing the rather grim set of his mouth. Coolly amused, she asked, 'Are you jealous?'

'Jealous? What the hell do you mean? *Patsy?* You're joking!'

'I don't see why I should be joking. She's very attractive, and desperately taken with you, and you seemed to be lapping it up.'

He had walked her to a corner of the deck, out of the wind, and in deep shadow. A slight warm breeze lifted her hair and cooled her bare shoulders above the *sulu* tied halter-fashion round her neck, and the water slapped rhythmically against the ship's sides far below them.

'Patsy isn't desperately taken with anyone but herself,' he said. 'I could almost think that *you* were jealous.'

'That's ridiculous!'

'Is it?' His arms came round her and pulled her close. 'And I wasn't lapping it up,' he added, his mouth touching her cheek, and wandering to her temple.

He tried to find her mouth, then, but she moved her head, evading him, and straining against his arms. 'You were thoroughly enjoying yourself,' she accused him. 'You thought it was all a huge joke!'

'I thought it was a mildly amusing situation,' he corrected. 'Good material for a farce, maybe, but not one I want to play in. Cass, please stop fighting me and let me kiss you. I've been wanting to do this all evening.'

He caught her head in his hands and made her face him, and his mouth came down on hers, hard and hungry, making her give a silent gasp of shocked surprise. His arms came about her, her head was cradled in the crook of one elbow, and her body brought tautly to his by the other arm about her waist.

She did stop fighting him after a few moments, and let herself drown in the mastery of his mouth on hers, and the satisfying strength of his arms.

His lips gentled and moved softly on hers, and his hands stroked her shoulders and back, lightly touching her skin as though the texture of it intrigued him.

He lifted his mouth at last, and held her quietly against him, his hands spread at her waist. 'Lovely girl,' he murmured. 'I want you—you know that, don't you?'

Cass let her head rest against his shoulder, her fingers splayed on the warmth of his chest, the silky shirt he wore hardly any barrier.

'Cass?' he whispered softly, his breath cooling her temple. 'What are you thinking?'

She was thinking that she wanted him, too, quite shockingly, considering she had only known him for a few days. She was thinking that she almost wished he would simply sweep her right off her feet and not give her time to think, and that she loved him for not doing it, for giving her the choice. And she was thinking that this couldn't possibly be love, it was much too sudden and too fierce; it had to be simple sexual infatuation. And that she wished her stupid emotions would catch up with the rational workings of her mind.

'I think,' she said, 'I'd better go down to my cabin.'

Lucien laughed softly, almost groaned. 'Oh, Cass, my lovely!' His lips trailed across her forehead, and then were on her neck and shoulder, warm and definitely seductive. 'Are you sure you're not that sort of a girl?' he asked.

'I'm sure I don't want to be,' she answered, pushing firmly against his hold.

He let her go. 'Moral scruples?'

'Laugh if you want to,' she said steadily.

But he sounded quite serious when he answered, 'I'm not laughing. I'll take you down.'

'No—please. I'd just as soon go alone.'

'If that's what you want.'

It was, because if he kissed her again outside her cabin, or even asked her on the way down to change her mind and come to his, she wasn't at all sure she wouldn't perhaps weaken. She was bewildered and almost frightened. How could an attraction so strong have grown in only a few days? She had been kissed before, had thought herself in love once or twice, had been propositioned more than once, but she had never been in serious danger of losing her head like this. This was something new. And why *him*, of all people? As if her feelings weren't confused enough without the added complication of knowing that she had to get an interview, and make a confession, sooner or later.

CHAPTER FOUR

THE next day, after a swim in the pool below the sun-deck, Cass and Lucien were watching a lively game of deck quoits, leaning back on the stern rail and commenting on the players' prowess.

She looked at him, smiling lazily, his eyes crinkled against the glare of the scrubbed deck and white paint-work, and thought how handsome he looked like that, with casual trousers pulled on over his swim shorts, and a bare torso, browned by the sun. He turned to her and raised his brows, catching her glance.

Cass looked away, applauding a good shot by one of the players, knowing that Lucien's eyes were still on her. 'You think too much, Cass,' he said softly. 'Why not just enjoy the moment?'

His voice sounded persuasive. He had a particularly pleasant voice, she realised, almost accentless, if that was possible, deep and cultured, without affectation. It was one of the things she had liked about him from the first . . .

'Is that your philosophy?' she asked him, smiling slightly.

He shrugged. 'Here—yes. That's what a holiday cruise is all about, isn't it? Leave your everyday life behind, and come away to the tropics—a romantic dream world where anything is possible, and there are no problems. For all we know the world might have ended in the last week or so. We've had no newspapers, no television, no radio broadcasts . . .'

'I'm sure the captain and his crew are in touch with

the world,' she said.

He laughed and put his hand over hers on the rail. 'Hi, you two!'

Patsy tripped towards them on high-heeled sandals, dressed in tight pink trousers and a brief flowered top, and clinging to the arm of the man who had been playing chess with Lucien when Cass first saw him.

Lucien straightened, and Cass automatically smiled and murmured, 'Hello, Patsy.'

Brightly, Patsy said, 'I've just been telling Hal what perfect sweeties you two are, taking pity on poor little me last night. It was awfully nice of you to invite me to join your cosy little twosome. And we did have a good time, didn't we?'

Her eyes were sending frantic, rather pathetic little messages, quite at variance with the bright smile fixed on her mouth and the determined gaiety of her breathless, little-girl voice.

Cass said swiftly, 'We enjoyed it, too, Patsy.' And Lucien said to the other man, 'Pity you couldn't have joined us. It was quite an evening.'

'Oh, poor sweet,' the girl cooed, stroking the arm she was clinging to. 'He's been so seasick! Haven't you, darling?' She pouted prettily, looking up at her companion's face and dripping sweet sympathy.

Darling grunted something that might have been agreement, and Cass thought charitably that he was probably still feeling seedy. He looked remarkably glum, with hunched shoulders and an almost aggressive way of poking his head forward and glaring at his feet.

As though to make up for his morose silence, Patsy laughed and said, 'Oh, I'm so sorry! You haven't met Cass, have you, darling? Cass, this is——'

'We've met.' He raised his head briefly and nodded

curtly to Cass, then said, 'We'll see you, then,' and turned abruptly, taking Patsy with him. She turned to say over her shoulder, ''Bye, you two!' as he almost dragged her through the nearest doorway from the deck.

Rather bemused, Cass met Lucien's laughing eyes. 'Are they married?' she asked him.

The humour in his eyes deepened. 'Not exactly,' he drawled, watching for her reaction.

'Oh.' She felt distinctly foolish. 'But Patsy's so pretty—and young. What on earth is the attraction?'

'She's very attracted to his money.'

'You're awfully cynical.'

Lucien shrugged. 'You asked. You see, Patsy is definitely "that sort of girl" when she smells money.'

Slightly nettled, Cass said unthinkingly, 'Is he richer than *you* are?'

There was the slightest of pauses before he asked, 'What makes you think I'm rich?'

She had already realised her mistake. She took a moment to recover, and then said, 'Well, Patsy was making a dead set at *you* last night. Don't tell me you hadn't noticed.'

'I noticed. And Patsy isn't the only one, is she?'

Cass went hot all over. She met his eyes for a moment, found them rather enigmatic, penetrating and questioning. She turned abruptly and leaned over the rail, watching the white wake of the ship curling behind them, cutting through water that was blue-black.

Lucien turned too, and touched her hand. 'Why did you throw yourself—or at least your worldly goods—at my feet?' he asked.

Cass tried to move her hand away, but his fingers tightened on hers, holding them down on the sun-warmed wood of the railing. He asked, 'Was it because you thought I was rich?'

Truthfully, she said, 'No, that—wasn't the reason. I—wanted to meet you.'

'Don't look so upset, Cass,' he said gently. 'I was very flattered—once I was sure that you had no ulterior motive.'

Cass closed her eyes tightly for a moment. This was getting worse and worse. 'Lucien—I——'

But he was going on, saying, 'You needn't have bothered, you know. I'd seen you through that window, and I'd have made sure that we met, believe me.'

She turned her head at last and looked at him. He was smiling, very sure of himself. Well, she supposed he had reason. With sudden certainty, she said, 'I'm not the first girl to throw myself at your feet, am I?'

The laughter faded from his face. 'No,' he said shortly. 'But their motivation is usually transparently clear. It isn't my fatal charm that attracts them, you see——' he paused, and then said, rather ruefully, 'Cass, I have a confession to make. I haven't been quite as honest as you.'

Something inside her twisted painfully. And at the same time a shamed hope began to stir. He was going to tell her who he really was—it could be the chance she was waiting for. If he owned up to deceiving *her*, he could hardly be too censorious when he found out about her real motive for waylaying him that first day.

'What do you mean?' she asked, as he paused, looking down at their entwined hands.

'Cass, I'm not exactly a businessman. I'm a film director. I thought, when you bumped into me so deliberately, that you might have been a would-be actress, looking for an easy way to break into films. It does happen—not often, but—well, I've learned to be wary.'

It wasn't what she had expected. Here he was, making a thing of being honest, and she knew he was lying to her. A black, bitter sense of disappointment almost overwhelmed her. But she had to say something to break the silence. Desperately, she tried a light laugh. It sounded a bit high and forced. She said, 'Well, I was so clumsy about it, you must have decided I was no actress!'

'Not a very good one, certainly. It wasn't long before I discovered you had no experience of acting, and not much interest, either.'

Still, I must be better at it than either of us realises, Cass thought. She started to say, 'Actually——' but then hesitated. He *wasn't* being honest with her, he was making an excuse for his suspicions of her. This was getting more complicated by the minute. How would he react if she told him the truth?

Oh, what a tangled web . . . she thought.

A round of applause made them look round, to find that the quoits game had finished. Lucien said, 'Come on, I'll give you a game.'

She was quite relieved, the conversation had been entering choppy waters, and this was a reprieve. She didn't play well, and Lucien laughed at her as he beat her roundly and then bore her off to the bar for a drink before dinner.

It wasn't until he had seen her down to her cabin later that evening, and kissed her goodnight at the door with a restrained passion, that it occurred to her to wonder if she had made a hideous mistake, after all. A film director—that meant feature films, surely. And the fledgling film industry in New Zealand, she was sure, just didn't support fulltime film directors. He couldn't be . . . though he did seem to know a lot about the other side of the camera, she remembered, recalling some of their conversations. It was certainly a subject that fired his interest. Maybe he did direct a few films—a millionaire could probably afford to indulge in an expensive hobby, a kind of extension of the home movie. Maybe he put some of his money into genuine films and had a finger in the pie of their making, but he *must* be Lionel Halliday. There simply wasn't anyone else on board who fitted. She was sure of that, now.

Nuku'alofa was their last port of call. Tonga, the Friendly Islands, lived up to the name. The ship was greeted by a police band playing on the wharf, and the people, brown-skinned and handsome Polynesians, were charming, courteous and helpful. Lucien hired a taxi and they explored the island, and the driver promised to take them to all the places of interest, starting with the royal palace. The palace was a fascinating piece of architecture, a Victorian baroque fantasy set in spacious grounds overlooking the water. After they had admired that to his satisfaction, their driver sped through the township of simple wooden houses and shops, and out into the countryside where the ubiquitous coconut palms and banana and breadfruit trees were interspersed with collections of houses, some in traditional style with woven matting walls and thatched roofs, and others made of wood and corrugated iron. Cass was touched by the wayside graveyards where the mounded sand was richly decorated with flowers, up-ended beer bottles arranged in intricate patterns, and large pictures and tapestries arranged over the graves of loved ones.

They drove along a narrow coastal road, almost level with the smooth sea, and had a look at the mysterious 'standing stones' which, the present King of Tonga had discovered, had been built on the same principle as Stonehenge, giving an accurate reading of the sun's movements at different times of the year.

The driver then took them on the tourist route to the ancient royal burial mounds, and the famous blow-hole where the sea fumed through a cleft in the rocks. Cass was glad when Lucien told the man to wait while they went for a walk along the narrow white strip of coral sand bounding the island. The roads were dusty, and the taxi was not over-endowed with springs. The quiet walk at the water's edge was a pleasant respite.

'Have you been here before?' she asked him. She knew he had travelled. He seemed to have a fairly extensive knowledge of Australia, England and America, and he had certainly known Suva. That much she had gathered from his conversation.

'Tonga?' he said. 'No, it's all new to me. As a matter of fact, I haven't seen a great deal of the Pacific at all. That's why I chose to do this cruise, and fill some lamentable gaps in my knowledge.'

'One day in each port?' she queried doubtfully. 'Have you learned much?'

'Enough to know which ones I'd like to revisit. And enough to get a few ideas . . .'

'Ideas?'

'For possible future films,' he said.

Cass looked away, her face a shuttered mask, and he said, 'I'm boring you. I'd forgotten you're not that interested.'

'I'm not bored,' she told him. But she didn't want him to spin a series of lies or half-truths to her. It hurt ridiculously that he had pretended to be frank, and then proceeded to thicken the web of deceit.

She walked to the water's edge and picked up a pink,

delicately frilled shell from the sand. 'Look,' she said. 'Isn't it beautiful? My souvenir of Tonga.'

Lucien's smile was wry. 'Yes,' he said, 'beautiful,' and he began to talk of something else.

On board, Cass packed the shell, first wrapping it carefully in tissue and then tucking it into a corner pocket of her suitcase. Lucien had kissed her before they returned to the taxi, a brief but warm kiss, almost passionless, and yet she had felt a ridiculous sense of yearning afterwards.

He kissed her again that night in the darkness of the top deck, where she had weakly allowed him to lead her, and this time he was less tender, drawing a wild response from her that made his eyes glitter as he reluctantly released her in answer to her agitated plea.

'Why?' he said harshly. 'Do you enjoy teasing men, Cass?'

'I'm *not* teasing!' she protested hotly. 'We'd better go back to the bar.'

But he caught her arm as she made to pass him, and pulled her back against him, his hand hard on her waist. His other hand caressed her hip and moved up to cup her breast. 'You don't really want to, do you?' he said in her ear. 'I can feel your heart beating, Cass. It's going like a trip-hammer. Kiss me again the way you did just now.'

He turned her firmly in his arms, and found her mouth with his. She struggled, uselessly, and then stayed still in his arms, taut and unyielding. His mouth lifted a little, and he took her head between his hands, muttering against her mouth, 'Come *on*, Cass. One kiss . . .'

His lips hardened and parted hers ruthlessly, and she knew he wasn't going to stop until she gave in. A moment longer she held out, then she relaxed against him, her hands going to his shoulders, her head falling back in submission, her mouth softening under the fierce impact of his . . .

But when his arms went about her again, his hands hauling her close and touching her with intimate caresses, she wrenched away her mouth and gasped, '*No!* That's enough, Lucien. That's all!'

He caught at her shoulders with a grip that hurt. 'Cass——!'

'You said one kiss!' she reminded him. 'I've given you that.'

For a moment his grip tightened. Then he let her go, and muttered, 'My God, you can certainly turn it on and off, can't you?'

'Please *don't!*' she whispered.

After a moment he said, more calmly, 'No. Sorry, I shouldn't have brought you out here.'

'I shouldn't have come,' she admitted.

'Why did you?'

She stammered, 'I—because—I don't know.'

'Because you like playing with fire? Is that it? Be careful, Cass. Little girls who get their kicks that way are likely to get burnt.'

She heard the note of grim warning in his voice, and knew that she was giving him every excuse for seduction. If she meant what she said, the logical thing to do was to make it clear she wouldn't be alone with him again. He was no boy to be played along with kisses. If only she didn't have to get that interview, she might have the sense and the strength to keep away from him, and ask him to keep away from her.

He took her back inside, and they danced. Cass shut her eyes and let him hold her close, with his cheek against her temple. He took her down to the cabin and kissed her lingeringly, then left her with faint derision in his eyes. There were four more nights to go before they landed again at Sydney.

She had made some notes of remarks he had made, things he had casually told her about himself and his life. There wasn't much. They tended to talk of the moment, or of impersonal subjects, but he had mentioned his mother, once, with affection, and said that she had died when he was a teenager. And another time he had talked about a sister in America, and a period when he had stayed with her and her husband and young family. Sometimes Cass wondered if she could take the cowardly way out and work these odd comments and remarks into a bogus interview, but she knew in her more rational moments that it wouldn't do. It was dishonest journalism, and anyway, if Lucien found out he might be entitled to sue. Rudy wouldn't relish that.

There weren't many opportunities on board to be private and alone in the daytime. Lois had once said, with an air of discovery, that she didn't know how people got lurid ideas about the sexual adventures that supposedly took place on cruise ships. Nearly everyone was sharing a cabin with at least one other person, and with nearly twelve hundred people on board including the crew, there simply wasn't enough privacy anywhere for clandestine affairs to be carried on.

'Are you planning an affair?' Cass asked.

'Heavens, no! I'm enjoying myself tremendously, but I don't want to get into deep water. What about you? Is it serious, with Lucien?'

Cass shook her head. 'Like you,' she said, 'I don't want to go off the deep end.'

But she was dreadfully afraid that she had. She had fallen in love so quickly she could scarcely believe it herself. And there was no future in it, because even if Lucien was obviously attracted, and he made no secret of that, he had no sort of permanence in mind. And the real reason she had hesitated so long over telling him she wanted an interview, of course, was simply that she was afraid, given his reputation for disliking the press and any form of publicity, that he would not want to see her again.

Once she had faced that, her mind began to work rather more rationally. Obviously if she wanted an interview she was going to have to tell him, some time. He might be angry, but there were still a few days left in which to persuade him. She would have to speak to him soon.

But not today, she decided. Tonight there was a gala ball, and the ship was humming with preparation. She wanted tonight to remember, if the fragile glass of illusion was going to be shattered by her revelations, if Lucien wanted nothing more to do with her afterwards.

The main lounge had been decorated with streamers and paper flowers and balloons for the occasion, and the passengers entered into the spirit of the evening by dressing in their most glamorous clothes and being almost feverishly lighthearted. Patsy was there in a figure-fitting gold dress, pushing her still glowering partner around the dance floor. He was one passenger who wasn't joining in the general hilarity.

Cass couldn't help a small laugh, and Lucien looked down at her and asked, 'What's the joke?'

'Your friend over there doesn't seem to be enjoying himself, does he?'

He followed her gaze and said, 'He's hardly a friend. I've played chess with him once or twice.'

'Is that the only shipboard entertainment he's interested in? I've scarcely seen him during the trip.'

Lucien said dryly, 'He brought Patsy along to entertain him.'

'You seem to know a lot about them.'

'Not a lot. But Patsy isn't exactly the soul of discretion.'

'The poor man can't still be seasick, can he? The sea's been like glass today.'

'Yes. Shall we go out and look at it?'

Cass met his eyes briefly, and shook her head. 'There's nothing to see, in the dark.'

Lucien smiled and went on dancing, but his hands pulled her closer to him, and when the music finished and they sat down, he kept his arm about her, and his fingers softly caressed her shoulder as they talked.

'I like that,' he said, taking a fold of the chiffon of her dress in his finger and thumb. It was pale apricot, cut with a full, softly falling skirt and a brief bodice.

'Thank you.' Cass looked down at his hand, lean and long-fingered. Her hair hid her expression from him, and he brushed it back behind her ear with his fingers, and when she turned to look at him, dropped a quick kiss on her lips.

Cass drew back.

Lucien's hand on her arm tightened a fraction, and he kissed her shoulder, his warm mouth sending an odd shiver down her spine. 'Don't,' she protested.

His eyes laughed at her. 'What's the matter? Too public for you? I've offered you a remedy for that.'

'I won't go outside with you,' she said stubbornly.

The hand on her arm moved to her nape, caressing it, and the other hand lifted hers to his mouth. He kissed her inner wrist, and she felt his tongue moving over the fine veins. She tugged her hand away, and saw the laughter and challenge in his eyes as they rested on her flushed face. 'Stop teasing me, Lucien!'

Her voice was a fierce whisper, and her eyes defied his.

'I'm not teasing, Cass. I'm making love to you.' His hand wandered to her cheek and down to her throat and the smooth skin above her bodice. He looked down, following the path of his fingers, and she saw the leashed, lazy desire in his eyes and caught her breath. 'Stop it,' she repeated, 'or I'll slap you!'

Lucien looked up then, a gleam of speculation in his eyes. 'Would you?'

'*Yes!*'

He grinned. 'I believe you would, sweet Cass.'

The music began again, and he pulled her to her feet, saying, 'Let's dance.'

He held her closely when they danced, and she thought it was really another way of making love, but sanctioned by custom, and wondered whether she was being hypocritical, or prudish, or both. When they sat down again, Lucien held her hand in his as he ordered drinks, and for the rest of the evening it was the only intimacy he offered when they were off the dance floor.

While the last dance was played, the lights dim and the music dreamy and romantic, his hands on her waist held her to him, and his thighs moved against hers. When the music drifted to a close, he didn't loosen his hold, but, standing there in the middle of the dance floor, he said in her ear, 'I'd like to take you below and make love to you.'

Reluctantly, she tried to move away, but he still held her.

'Cass?' His voice was low and urgent. She looked up, saw the smouldering light in his eyes, and said, 'Please don't ask me.'

His mouth twisted at the corner. 'Afraid you might say yes?'

She bit her lip and nodded.

'Oh, God! You darned exasperating little idiot!' He released her abruptly, only to grab her wrist in an unbreakable grip.

'Lucien!' she protested, as he dragged her with him from the lounge to the deck outside.

He gave her a glance and said uncompromisingly, 'Shut up.'

Shocked, she closed her lips tightly, and he found a secluded part of the deck and swung her to face him, her back against the bulkhead.

Furiously, she demanded, 'What do you think you're doing?'

'I'm going to make you say yes!'

She tried to push past him, but his arms came round her and held her helpless while he kissed her mouth with a relentless passion. Every attempt at escape was frustrated by his arms and the hardness of his body, and his mouth continued its remorseless assault on her defences.

But she had a new defence now. She hadn't consented to this, he had forced her to come with him, forced her to accept his lovemaking, and that made her angry, so that a simmering sense of outrage warred with the terrible temptation to give in to him.

When he whispered against her mouth, 'Kiss me, Cass,' she set her teeth stubbornly and said, 'No!'

Her head was bent back under the pressure of his mouth on hers, and he began to caress her with his hands. But when she freed one of her hands and tried to hit out at him, he caught it and twisted it behind her, and his other hand tangled into her hair, stilling her frantic efforts to escape the invasion of his kiss.

Suddenly terrified by her helplessness, she felt tears sliding hotly down her cheeks, and Lucien tasted them.

He pulled away suddenly, releasing her hands, his fingers touching her wet cheeks. 'Oh, hell!' he exclaimed harshly. 'Don't cry!'

He brought her close to him again, but his touch was different now, gently soothing as his hands stroked her shoulders and his fingers brushed back her hair. 'Don't,' he said again. 'I'm sorry, I didn't mean to frighten you.'

Trying to stifle her sobs against his shirt, she said shakily, 'I don't know what else you meant.'

'You're not *that* innocent,' he told her grimly. 'But it was seduction I had in mind, not rape.'

Cass raised a hand to wipe the tears from her face, and he said, 'I know I'm supposed to have a snow-white handkerchief all ready to offer you, but I'm afraid I'm not properly equipped.' He dug in his pocket and asked, 'Will a blue one do? It's got a rather nice brown border, and it's clean, though rather crumpled, I'm afraid.'

She gave an unsteady little laugh. 'It's all right, I'm not fussy. Thank you.' She half turned from him and wiped her eyes and nose. 'I'm sorry, I'm not really a tearful sort of person.'

'I'm the one who's supposed to be grovelling. I didn't hurt you, did I?'

She shook her head. 'Not really. You did warn me about playing with fire.'

'So I did. Well, you've found an effective method of dealing with the blaze.'

'It wasn't deliberate,' she said.

'No, I realise that.'

She folded the dampened handkerchief and returned

it, and there was an awkward little silence. She felt
horribly depressed and ashamed. It seemed so utterly
futile to burst into tears because a man had kissed her,
like some insipid Victorian miss.

'Well,' said Lucien lightly, 'anticlimax, I'm afraid.
I'll take you down to your cabin.'

She felt too exhausted and unhappy to object. He
would probably insist, anyway.

Outside her door, she turned to him and asked, 'Will
I see you tomorrow, Lucien?' She saw the sardonic
surprise in his face, and added quickly, 'There's
something I want to tell you. It's—important.'

A faint frown settled between his brows, and he said,
'Of course I'll see you, if that's what you want. I'll
catch up with you before lunch. In the small bar, forward?'

'Yes, thank you.'

'I don't know what for.'

He looked wry, and she told him, 'I had a lovely
evening.'

'Until I spoiled it.'

'It isn't spoiled. You've been very—understanding.'

'Coals of fire, Cass. Go on in. I'll see you tomorrow.'

CHAPTER FIVE

HAVING decided to put her cards on the table, Cass suffered from a combination of relief and nervousness.

The small bar was not crowded when Lucien found her waiting for him, her hands clenched in her lap, creasing the skirt of the cream cotton frock she wore, and her smile apprehensive as she studied his face, finding it difficult to read.

'Drink?' he asked her as he took a seat on the other side of the narrow table.

Cass said no, then changed her mind, thinking she could do with some Dutch courage, and she sat in uneasy silence until it came, wondering for the hundredth time how she was going to word her confession. Lucien didn't speak either, just sat looking at her as he might look at a rather pleasant painting hanging on a wall. When the glass was set in front of her she lifted it thankfully to her lips, and gulped down several hasty mouthfuls.

Lucien raised his brows, his own drink held in his hand as he watched her. Catching that look, Cass glanced quickly away, as he lifted his glass at last and took a leisurely sip, still watching her. When he lowered it again, he said, 'You said you had something to tell me.'

The moment of truth, Cass thought wildly, and took a deep breath.

Lois's voice broke in with, 'Hello, you two! Drinking this early?'

Cass nearly jumped. She had been concentrating so

hard on what she would say that she hadn't noticed Lois and Trevor coming into the bar. Now they stood smiling expectantly, and Lucien got to his feet, pulled out a chair for Lois and invited, 'Join us. Then you'll be in no position to criticise.'

Momentarily she closed her eyes. Frustration warred with guilty relief. She could put off the moment for a little longer.

The conversation was lively, but she took scant part in it, only smiling and nodding at the appropriate moments. There was a general opinion that the cruise had been tremendous fun, and regret that it was coming to an end, and Lois and Trevor had a fund of stories and anecdotes of shipboard life which Lucien could cap with stories of his own. But now and then she caught him looking at her with speculation in his eyes.

Trevor bought another round of drinks, and just when the conversation began to flag, Lois looked about at the rapidly growing number of people in the bar, and said, 'Oh, by the way, we've discovered the millionaire! He's a property developer from New Zealand; his real name's Halliday, but he's calling himself Mr Scott. That's him, over there with the blonde girl— you were talking to her the other night, weren't you, Cass?'

Cass had gone cold, nearly choking on her drink. With precision she put down her glass and instinctively looked where Lois had indicated. She recognised Patsy and the nondescript 'Hal' who was her escort. 'No,' she said positively, 'you're wrong, Lois.'

'She isn't, you know,' Lucien said calmly. 'I told you he had money, Cass.'

Cass looked again at the man who called himself Hal Scott, and was suddenly blindingly aware that he had

pale grey eyes, that his hair which she had seen as
sandy or pepper-and-salt could have been described as
brown, that the face in the photographs might easily
be this man's face. Her head jerked to face Lucien,
and she blurted out, 'But—oh *no*! I thought it was
you!'

Dismay was written all over her face, she couldn't
hide it. Lois gave a crow of disbelieving laughter and
said, 'Cass! You never *said*, you dark horse!' and
Trevor grinned and said, 'You've backed the wrong
one, Cass. We promised faithfully not to let on who
told us, but *that's* Halliday, all right.'

Lucien was sitting very still, looking at her, and her
heart gave a sudden plunge as she realised that his eyes
had gone icy, his mouth thinning into a faint sneer.
'Did you, Cass?' he said softly. 'Well, that explains a
lot.'

With some inkling of what he meant, she began,
'No—Lucien, you don't understand——'

'I do now,' he said. He finished his drink in one
quick movement and put down the glass, glancing at
his watch and rising immediately to his feet. 'Sorry to
break up the party,' he said pleasantly, 'but I have to
go. Have a good time for what remains of the trip, all
of you.'

He nodded to them and left, even as Cass stumbled
to her feet and tried to move past Trevor, whose long
legs blocked her exit. By the time he had moved them
out of the way and got up to let her through, Lucien
had disappeared through the doorway, and when Cass
dashed out he was gone, nowhere in sight.

Lois and Trevor looked concerned as she returned
slowly to the table. 'Did we put a foot in?' Trevor
asked frankly, and she smiled wanly and said, 'It
doesn't matter. He got the wrong idea, that's all.'

Lois said, 'Sorry, Cass, I didn't realise——'

'I know. It's all right. It really doesn't matter.'

'Does he think you're a gold-digger or something?' Lois asked curiously. 'I don't believe it, even if you *did* think he was this man Halliday. You're not the type.'

Trevor looked doubtful and decidedly uncomfortable, and Cass said, 'Thanks, Lois. I'm not. I'm a journalist, actually. I was supposed to do a story on the Halliday man. I haven't a prayer, now.'

'Why not? Go and ask him.'

Cass shook her head. 'I don't think it would work. He's very press-shy, by all accounts. That's why—oh, it's all too complicated to explain.'

'Well, there's no harm in asking, is there?' Lois said reasonably. 'He can always say no.'

So he could, Cass thought. Certainly she was going to have no time to create any kind of impression now. Two more days to go ... She looked round at the couple who were sitting together in a corner, Patsy in a provocative pose with legs crossed and one foot swinging a high-heeled sandal on her toes, and the man staring morosely into his drink. As she watched, he looked up and gave a faint smile at something Patsy said, though, and perhaps it was that that decided her. At least she could give it a try.

'Okay, I will,' she said, and rose quickly before discretion got the better part of valour. She went across to the table and smiled brightly, saying, 'Hello, Patsy—Hal. May I join you?'

He stared, and her heart sank slightly. Patsy, after a moment of surprise, gave her a brilliant smile and said, 'Sure! Help yourself!' She turned to the man and said, 'You remember Cass, don't you, Hal?'

Hal gave her a cold, encompassing stare, registered a

slight interest as his eyes lingered on the low neck of her dress and the curve of her breasts, and resumed his bored study of his drink.

It wasn't very promising, but Cass decided to plunge right in. She said, 'I've just discovered who you are, Mr Halliday. I promise I won't spread the word, but I wonder if you could find time to talk to me for a little while—perhaps later in the day? Any time it suits you.'

'Talk?' he said, and his eyes met hers again, insolently suggestive.

Her skin crawled with dislike. Close to, he was an unpleasant little man, she decided. She was very sorry for Patsy, even if she had gone into this with her eyes open. Firmly, she said, 'I'll be frank with you, Mr Halliday. I'm a reporter for *Citymag*. I would very much like to——'

'I don't speak to reporters,' he interrupted.

'I'm not a news reporter,' she persisted. 'What we have in mind is an in-depth interview, giving you a chance to put your own point of view, express your opinions.'

'I'm not interested.'

'I shouldn't have sprung it on you so suddenly, perhaps,' she said doggedly, 'but I didn't know until just a few minutes ago who you were. Would you please think about it? If you should change your mind, this is my cabin number.' She scribbled the number on a page from her diary, added her name and put it on the table before him, since he made no move to take it. 'I promise I won't misrepresent what you say,' she assured him. 'You might find it could do your public image a lot of good.'

Glancing at the small piece of paper before him, he said, 'When you have as much money as I have, Miss

Reynolds, you don't have to worry about your public image.'

'May I quote that?' she asked him quickly.

'No, you'll quote nothing. I told you, I don't talk to reporters.' He got up abruptly, and dragged at Patsy's arm, jerking her up beside him. Patsy gave Cass an apologetic smile and scooped up the diary page. 'I'll try and persuade him,' she whispered, then turned to follow him. As they neared the door, Cass saw her take his arm and tuck the piece of paper into his jacket pocket, talking rapidly, her small, pretty face turned winningly to his.

She haunted the cabin all day, but the cream phone on the desk top didn't ring. So much for Patsy's persuasion, she thought resignedly. Well, she might be looking for a new job when she got home. But even worse was the fact that Lucien despised her as a mercenary little cheat.

She tried to speak to him that evening, but he turned away when he saw her coming towards him, and left her burningly embarrassed, sure that everyone around had seen the snub and was either laughing at her or feeling sorry for her. Anger helped. He needn't have been so beastly about it, after all. He might have at least deigned to listen to an explanation.

The next day was their last at sea, and although they had left tropical waters and were rapidly steaming towards Sydney, the sun shone and tempted many of the passengers into the pools on deck. Cass took a dip with Lois and was lying on the warm deck afterwards making the most of the last opportunity to enhance her suntan, when she felt someone watching her. She looked up and saw Lionel Halliday staring over the railing above, looking down on the sunbathers, and on her in particular, his eyes assessing the slim figure revealed by her flowered bikini. She flushed, and sat up, and he nodded to her. About to ignore him and turn her back, she thought better of it, and stiffly returned his nod before pulling her towel around her shoulders. Hope was fading fast, but she certainly couldn't afford to snub the man, if there was any faint chance of still getting that interview.

When she and Lois were tidying up in their cabin before lunch, the phone rang, and she answered it.

'It's Patsy,' she heard. 'Hal says, if you still want that interview, you can come to the cabin after lunch.'

'Oh, Patsy, thank you!' she gasped. 'I don't know how you did it, but I'm very grateful.'

'Don't mention it. You were nice to me,' the girl said. 'Not many girls are nice to me.'

She could well imagine, Cass thought, but there wasn't much you could say to a remark like that. As she dropped the receiver back on its cradle, she clasped her hands together in glee. At last, something was going right for her!

Lois grinned happily for her when she explained, saying, 'Good for you! How about sending me a copy of the magazine? I haven't given you my address yet, have I?'

She wrote it down, and took down Cass's. 'To think it's nearly over,' she sighed. 'It's been so short, and yet home and work seem ages away. It's been fantastic, though, hasn't it? What a shame Trevor's from New Zealand. He said he'll write, but I don't suppose it will last. And you and Lucien—I guess there wasn't much future in it, anyway. He's Australian, isn't he?'

'Oh, no! At least——' Dismay struck her again. 'I suppose he probably is. Usually you can tell by the accent, but he hasn't really got one. But——' She had jumped to conclusions about him from the start, had started from a false premise, and built her knowledge of him around that. Now that she thought of it, he had talked more about Australia than New Zealand. She had assumed that it was one of the places he visited when he travelled, as he obviously did quite often. Now she realised that of course Lois was right. He didn't even live in the same country . . . they lived on opposite sides of the Tasman.

Determinedly she tried to brush aside the hollow feeling of depression in her stomach, with the practical thought that it was lunchtime and she was hungry. But she knew it was more than that. It was futile, foolish, to wish that things had been different . . .

She had no trouble finding the cabin number that Patsy had given her. Lionel Halliday opened it himself, and ushered her in, not exactly smiling, but at least in something approaching a friendly manner. There was a lot more space than in the cabin she shared with Lucy, and it had a sofa and two deep chairs with a coffee table set in one area, where he motioned her to sit down.

'Have a drink,' he suggested, going to a well-stocked refrigerator in one corner, another amenity which the ordinary cabins didn't boast. He might be travelling incognito, she thought, but he wasn't stinting on his little luxuries.

She asked for a gin and tonic, because he was pouring one for himself, and she thought he might be more relaxed if he wasn't drinking alone. As he handed it to her, she asked, 'Where's Patsy?'

He shrugged. 'I sent her out to play. She'd only distract us—can't stop talking.'

Well, that was probably true enough, but she had assumed Patsy would be here. It was disconcerting to find herself alone with him instead. Ridiculous, she assured herself. She didn't need a chaperone for a perfectly straightforward interview.

She had a tiny tape recorder in her bag, but when she pulled it out he queried, 'Do you have to use that thing?'

'Not if you don't want me to,' she said hastily. 'Some people prefer it, since there's less likelihood of being misquoted.'

'Don't you do shorthand?'

'Yes. I'll use that, if you'd rather I did.'

He nodded, and she put away the recorder and pulled out her notebook and pencil. She took it slowly at first, drawing him out with innocuous questions about his childhood and the beginnings of his business. By the time they had reached the more controversial part of his career, he had begun to boast of his achievements, and talk without prompting. Cass even dared to say straight out, 'Some people don't believe that anyone can make so much money legally, Mr Halliday.'

He surprised her by laughing. 'Don't they? Some people only eat sour grapes. And you called me Hal yesterday.'

She smiled. 'May I use that quote, Hal? It's a good line.'

He shrugged. 'Please yourself.'

'Well, I think that's all I need. Thank you so much for giving me your time. I'm very grateful, really. And knowing you don't like the press——'

'Some members of it,' he corrected, his eyes flickering over her. He got up. 'Have another drink.' He didn't wait for her to refuse, but was already pouring one. Cass took it, feeling it would be rude to refuse him, but she drank it rather quickly, eager to get away now that the interview was in the bag.

When she put the glass down and rose to leave, he stood with her, too close, and his hand ran down her bare arm. 'You're the prettiest member of the press I've seen,' he told her, in her ear. 'Especially in a bikini.'

Uneasily, she tried to move away. His hand clamped on her arm, and he said, 'Come on, Cass. You said you were grateful.'

'I am,' she said, pulling against his hold. 'But——'

'Well, show me,' he said suggestively, and his arms pinned her to him, while his mouth descended on hers in a greedy, sensual kiss.

Instinctively she recoiled from him, but his hold tightened and, realising it was useless to struggle, she maintained an icy indifference instead. Eventually he pushed her away in disgust. 'Can't stand frigid women!' he muttered. 'Patsy may be brainless, but at least she knows how to please a man.'

Cass bit back the furious remarks that sprang to her mind and said coldly, 'Thank you for the interview, Mr Halliday. I'll see that the editor sends you a copy.'

She swept out into the narrow passageway, snapping the door shut behind her, and paused there to regain her poise. She smoothed her hair back from her flushed cheeks and adjusted the neckline of her blouse, which had been pulled awry by his powerful embrace, and tucked the blouse more firmly into the waistband of her denim skirt. Then she took a deep breath and began to walk down the passageway—and was suddenly brought up short, her eyes widening with shock. Standing in the doorway of a nearby cabin was Lucien, and his face was a cold mask of contemptuous rage.

For a moment their eyes locked, and she had a sudden irrational impulse to turn and run from him.

Then her common sense reasserted itself, and she began walking again, as calmly as possible, making to pass him. She came abreast of him before he moved, suddenly shooting out a hand to take her arm in an unbreakable grip, and drawing her into the cabin with him. He had slammed the door behind her before she had time to say, her voice high with fright, 'What on *earth* do you think you're doing?'

He didn't answer, but his hands came up to her shoulders and he shook her briefly but hard, so that she let out a little cry of shock and fear, and her bag fell with a thud on to the carpet. Lucien stopped, and glared at her, while she stared back in frantic bewilderment. Finally she managed to say, 'Have you gone *mad*? Let me go!'

'Quite likely,' he muttered, but instead of letting her go, he jerked her closer and kissed her savagely, bending back her head under the onslaught until she thought her bones would snap. When he stopped, she was gasping for air, and only the strength of his hands held her up. 'Lucien!' she choked out. 'Lucien, stop it! You mustn't!'

'Mustn't I? Why not? Are you saving it all for Hal?'

She looked into eyes that were darkly furious, glittering and hard like diamonds. 'What are you talking about?' she asked shakenly.

'Don't pretend you don't know,' he jeered at her. 'I saw you go in there over an hour ago, and now you come out with his mark on you, as clear as——'

'*What?*' she cried. 'What *mark*?'

'Your whole appearance shouted it when you came out of that door,' he drawled, his eyes narrowing to unpleasant slits. 'You stood there looking flushed and freshly bedded, with your lipstick smudged off and your hair still tousled and your clothes thrown on in a hurry. What's the matter, is Patsy due back soon?'

Cass blinked, scarcely able to believe her ears. 'You've got a *filthy* mind!' she told him. 'I have *not* been to bed with Hal—not that it's any of your business! As a matter of fact I've been sitting there *talking* to him, for the last hour or so. I was——'

But he was laughing, loud and derisive. 'Do you expect me to believe that? Good heavens, I know I've been incredibly gullible with you, but I'm really not as stupid as I look, you know.'

'Gullible?'

'Yes. I swallowed every lie you handed me, didn't I? You didn't have an ulterior motive when you threw yourself at me, you just liked my looks. You liked making love to me, but your old-fashioned morals prevented you from following through. You had no idea what I do for a living, and you didn't care, you liked me for myself. Well, that was partly true, anyway. You didn't know, but you thought you did—a case of mistaken identity. And you played me along beautifully until Lois let the cat out of the bag. I thought then that the fact that you'd missed your objective after all should compensate me for my hurt feelings. I thought that at least your unwillingness to come to bed might have had genuine grounds. But you lost no time in giving Hal your cabin number, did you—and no time in offering to share his bed, either!'

'That's not true!'

'Don't bother to lie. I saw the number and your name—in your writing, too. He had it in his pocket when we were playing chess this morning. He put it on the table with a few other things when he was searching his pockets for his cabin key.'

'I did give him the number, but——'

'You're a fast worker, darling!'

'Stop it, Lucien! I'll explain if you——'

'Oh, don't bother. Explanations are so boring. I can think of much more interesting things to do!'

Angrily, she cried, 'Oh, you're being *ridiculous*!'

'Yes, maybe I have been,' he said. 'You must have had fun laughing up your sleeve while you kept me dangling.'

'I didn't!' She moved back sharply as he put hard hands on her waist, but he was stronger and very determined. She was pulled close to him, his hands holding her as she strained away from him, throwing back her head to look at him.

It was a mistake. He found her mouth with his and began to kiss her mercilessly, and when she pushed against his shoulders with her fists, he captured her hands in one of his and held them firmly behind her, then went on kissing her lips hard and searching and forceful.

Without moving his mouth from hers, he suddenly swung her into his arms, and in the next second she found herself flung down on a bed, with Lucien leaning over her, holding her protesting hands on either side of her head, and his mouth returned to its sensual punishment.

Cass became a prey to an extraordinary mixture of emotions—anger and despair mingled with desire. When his mouth shifted to her throat, and his hands left hers to tug open the buttons of her blouse, she gasped out, 'What are you doing?'

'Taking what you've been offering me all this time, but I was too damned stupidly polite to take before,' he said.

His hand pushed aside the soft fabric, and began caressing her skin, as she stiffened with hurt understanding and begged, 'Lucien, please—I haven't been offering—anything. You mustn't——'

'I know you're not necessarily in the mood,' he said. 'You've already had one lover this afternoon. But there's very little time, you see—And *I* intend to enjoy it.'

'Lucien, stop being so beastly! I was——'

He stopped her voice with his mouth, and this time he was gentler and more persuasive, so that she felt desire growing stronger than anger. For a few moments she relaxed, responding to him, and his hands touched her softly while his mouth moved over hers. He pushed aside her bra strap and as she felt his intrusive fingers she fought down the surge of pleasure and took advantage of his slackened hold to push him off balance and slide from the bed.

She stood up shakily, but before she could move a step, he had swung himself up to sit on the bed, and his hand encircled her wrist as he stood to join her.

'Let me go, Lucien,' she protested. 'I'm not going to sleep with you. I don't want——'

'Stop playing games,' he said tersely. 'You want me, all right. You weren't pretending just now—I could feel it.'

'Can't you understand a simple *no*?'

'Come *here*!' His hand jerked her close to him, his other hand coming up behind her head, but she evaded his mouth and said, 'Lucien, if you don't let me go, I'll scream!'

'Will you?' He suddenly half turned, and threw her back on to the bed, coming down on top of her as she felt her face tighten in panic at his unrelenting violence and the grim purpose in his face. Her lips parted and her breath sucked in, the scream completely involuntary, because she was frightened, more frightened than she had ever been in her life. She felt his hand clamp over her mouth, muffling the sound in her throat. Her eyes stared helplessly as he pinned her down with his weight and his fingers hurt the soft skin of her cheeks.

He stared back, and she saw the implacable temper fade from his eyes and the quick frown appear between them. Long moments elapsed, and he moved a hand and found the rapid beating of her heart. He said slowly, 'You really are scared, aren't you?'

Then he shifted his hand from her mouth, and Cass touched her lips with her tongue and whispered, 'Yes.'

She wasn't so much, now. For a few moments Lucien had been out of control, and she had been quite certain he intended to force her, but now his face had changed, and she knew that the danger was past.

He moved, and got up, looking down at her. 'Get up,' he said. 'I'm not going to attack you again.'

She moved slowly, not looking at him. One of her shoes had fallen off, and she fumbled it on again. He didn't help, just stood and watched her. She said, 'Lucien, I'm a journalist. All I wanted was an interview. That's what I was doing in Hal's cabin—interviewing him.' He was silent, and she said, 'If you don't believe me, look in my bag. There's a notebook there. Look!' She crossed the floor and picked up the bag from where it lay by the door. She found the notebook and opened it. 'See?'

'Shorthand,' he said. 'It could be your private "Trip Book" or even diary notes.'

'I tell you, I'm a journalist——'

'You never said so before—even just now, when I accused you of being with him.'

'You didn't give me a chance——'

'And why should I believe you now?' he asked.

No reason, she supposed. She couldn't deny that she had deceived him from the start. It had been a disastrous affair, all round. He could ask Hal, of course, perhaps he would. But she wasn't going to beg him to. Something ached inside, for what might have been. But there could be nothing for them, now. If he couldn't trust her, believe her, and she knew it, there was simply no future in it. So much for her shipboard romance.

Defeated, she said, 'I'm sorry, I didn't intend to make a fool of you, Lucien. I wish you could believe me.'

He didn't answer, and she sighed and said, 'Well, goodbye. I wish it hadn't ended like this.'

She let herself out, and he hadn't echoed her trite words. She wished she could have thought of something to say that would have broken down the barrier of distrust and disillusion, but apparently he had finished completely with her, and she couldn't blame him. There was simply no use in thinking, *If only* . . .

CHAPTER SIX

RUDY was pleased with the article. He never asked for details of how Cass had managed to get the interview with Lionel Halliday, and she didn't volunteer any. He did ask her if she had uncovered any hint of dirty dealings in Halliday's business life, and she said, shortly, 'He wasn't telling, and he didn't give away any clues, either.'

'Okay,' Rudy shrugged. 'We'll run it straight. Good stuff, Cass.'

It was his highest accolade, and weeks ago she would have been over the moon at having earned it. Now, she found it meant very little. It was ages before she shook off the hollow feeling of misery that had accompanied her home, and began to take a real interest in her work and her social life again.

It couldn't last for ever, though. Quite soon there was an assignment that was stimulating and challenging enough to engage her interest to the exclusion of humiliating and embarrassing memories, and gradually she learned to live with an aching sense of loss, until the sharpness of the pain faded and finally became only an occasional unexpected twinge, brought on by magazine pictures of tropical islands or travel brochures for Pacific holidays. Cass had never been the type to brood over what might have been.

The magazine prospered, and she was regarded as one of its best staffers. She enjoyed the work immensely, and knowing that she was good, and recognised as good, gave her increased self-confidence as well as a very good salary. She never suffered from a shortage of available attractive men to include in her social life, and eventually, inevitably, there was one who became special.

His name was Dave Mercer, and he was a fairly brilliant young lawyer. Cass met him when she was doing interviews for a series on 'Men and Women of the Future' which was supposed to identify young Aucklanders who were tipped for important positions in society over the next few decades. She had liked Dave because he obviously found the idea of being in the series rather amusing, but was willing to go along with it to please her. He had talked easily, in a slightly tongue-in-cheek way, about the possibility of becoming a member of the judiciary some day, and had laughed when she asked if he would like to be Minister of Justice.

He had invited her to dinner with him before the interview was concluded, and she accepted without hesitation. It was the beginning of a relationship which progressed from liking to something much more. Dave said he was in love with her, but Cass was more cautious. She didn't want to get in too deeply too soon. She liked him a lot, found his kisses and mild love-making very pleasant, and returned them with warmth. When he wanted to progress beyond that, she fended him off easily, and although he seemed rather amused at her circumspection he didn't object. Cass thought that was as it should be, and told herself she had to be in love with him. The wistful, barely acknowledged thought at the back of her mind, that she didn't feel the wild emotion with Dave that she had once experienced with Lucien Hale, was not important. It had been an adolescent fantasy. What she had with Dave was surely more solid and enduring, and far less dangerous, than that emotional storm, an unreal interlude that had ended in pain and disillusion and anger.

That short period of her life was one she did her utmost to forget. She wanted nothing more than what she had now—a rewarding job, an independent home life, with her own small flat near her work, and a promising relationship with a very nice and attractive young man whose future prospects were as good as her own.

When Rudy called her into his office one day, she had no idea as she followed him and took the chair before his cluttered desk that all this was about to be threatened.

'Got a special assignment for you,' he said, without preamble. 'There's an Aussie film company coming over here to make a new feature film. They'll be working mainly on a private beach north of Waiwera. I've got permission to send a reporter and photographer up there for a week to live with the crew, watch the filming and report on what's happening. They're quite keen to get some favourable publicity. Some local film-makers aren't too happy about the idea, apparently. There's a bit of grumbling going on— sour grapes, perhaps.'

'Well, it does seem a bit of a cheek, doesn't it?' Cass asked mildly. 'After all, Australia's an awfully big place, and their film industry is much bigger than ours, too. World class, now, whereas our people are still trying to make it big in the international stakes. Why should they decide to make their film here?'

Rudy leaned back and looked at her thoughtfully. 'Ask him,' he said, pushing a piece of paper towards her over the surface of the desk. He stabbed a smoke-stained finger at the signature at the foot of the typewritten letter. 'He's the director. See if he can justify his decision to our readers. It should make an interesting slant for the article—we might even box it on the page, if he sounds good. You can make it in-depth, by the way, the article. I want to spread it over half a dozen pages. Description of what they're doing, why they want to do it here, how they plan to do it, and various interviews—the stars, of course, and the director, and—well, anyone you think will make good copy.'

But he had lost her. Cass had automatically picked up the letter and turned it to read the signature. And she was staring at it as though the bold black scrawl was about to leap from the page and bite her. It was legible enough, but the name was neatly typewritten below it, too, so that there was no possibility of a mistake. *Lucien Hale*.

'Send someone else!' she said at last, her voice sounding oddly high and strained.

'What?' Rudy looked as though he thought she was slightly deranged. 'Why should I?'

'I don't want to spend a week out in the wop-wops,' she said feebly.

'*Waiwera?* Girl, it's practically suburban these days! The city buses go that far, for Pete's sake! Or nearly, anyway. It's—what?—an hour's drive, I suppose, or possibly a bit more. If you don't want to leave the boy-friend for that long he can pop up and see you, or you can drive down and meet him for an evening on the town.'

'It's not that.'

'I should hope not! What is it, then?'

'I don't want to do it. You said they want some favourable publicity. I think I feel the same as the local film boys. Why should Australians steal our limelight?

I'm prejudiced. I'm not suitable.'

'Oh, yeah?' Rudy leaned back in his chair, and pursed his lips. 'I said they'd like the publicity to be favourable. I didn't promise them it would be. You can be sure of that. Our readers have come to expect unbiased reporting from us, and you know it. What's more, *they* know it. That's why they were willing to let us in on this. It's up to them to convince us—*you*—that they're not taking bread out of the mouths of innocent Kiwis with their fillm. And I trust you, Cass. Even when you admit you're biased on a subject, you're able to write good, balanced stuff. You know it, and I know it. You did it when we covered the factory-versus-the-environmentalists story just a couple of months ago. And you even did it on the abortion issue. I wouldn't have let anyone else handle that hot potato. Okay, so you're against it unless it's a genuine life-or-death situation, but no one would have guessed that from your story. I even had letters from anti-abortion groups accusing you of being biased to the *other* side.'

'Maybe I leant over too far backwards not to let my own feelings come through.'

'Rot! I got just as much mail from the pro-abortion people accusing us of prejudice against them. You did a good job. And you can do it again.'

'That was an important issue. This is—trivial in comparison. A whole week watching people making a film. It's Sunday paper stuff, Rudy. I don't want to do it.'

Rudy frowned. 'What's the matter with you? Filming is a multi-million-dollar industry, as well as an art form. It means overseas funds for us if we ever do make the big time from New Zealand. Sure, there are trivial films. But the whole question can't be dismissed as trivial, Cass. You surprise me.'

'It sounds boring! Can't you get someone else?'

'You know, when people make lots of excuses, they're usually not coming up with the real reason. Like to tell me it?'

Cass looked at him warily. 'All right,' she said. 'It's—personal. I met this man once, and I don't like him. What's more, he can't stand me, either. Now, let me off the hook, Rudy?'

His gaze sharpened, and she could almost see his brain ticking over. He rubbed his chin absently and she saw a gleam light his eye. 'I don't know,' he said slowly. 'It could be an advantage. Give the writing a bit of bite——'

'*Rudy!*' Cass leaned on the desk, wanting to shake the man. 'It would *not* make a better story! It would just be horribly embarrassing for both of us. *Find someone else!*'

He looked disgruntled, but said, 'Okay, I'll send Pete. Seeing you refuse to do it, for *personal* reasons.'

'Don't be nasty,' Cass said calmly. 'I didn't refuse to do it at all. I just gave you a perfectly good reason for sending someone else, that's all.'

'It took you long enough to get round to it. And I'm still not sure it *is* a good reason,' he grumbled.

Cass smiled and turned to go, and Rudy added, 'You're not the meek and mild little miss who started work here a couple of years ago, are you? Don't let success go to your head.'

She looked back, her hand on the door knob and said, 'No, sir.'

'Oh, get out!' he growled as she opened the door. She was laughing as she closed it behind her.

The laughter faded rather quickly, though. It had

given her a nasty jolt, seeing Lucien's name appear out of the blue like that. For a few minutes she remembered vividly their bitter parting, and what had gone before. No, she certainly didn't want to see him, ever again.

She was unsettled for the remainder of the day, and angry with herself because of it. It was all water under the bridge now. And yet every so often the image of Lucien Hale's dark face intruded on her mind, and she had to thrust it firmly back into the recesses of her subconscious. She was glad that she had a date with Dave that night, something to take her mind off the persistent, recurring memories.

They saw an award-winning film, and afterwards ate at one of the city's Chinese restaurants. Cass had a liking for Chinese cooking, and sometimes tried her hand at it herself. Early in their acquaintance she had discovered that Dave shared her taste, and they often 'ate Chinese'.

He came to her flat later and she gave him coffee. When he put down the cup and pulled her down beside him on the sofa, she snuggled willingly into his arms, and was annoyed to find that as he kissed her she kept recalling other arms about her, other lips on hers, not soft and coaxing like Dave's but compelling and passionate.

Trying to banish the pictures filling her wayward mind, she moved closer to the man who held her now, and wound her arms about him almost desperately, kissing him back with a feverish intensity.

She felt his surprise in a sudden stillness, before he gathered her tightly against him and his mouth hardened and forced hers open so that he could kiss her deeply.

Panic and dismay flashed through her. She had invited this, she knew it. And she knew equally clearly that she didn't want it. For a few minutes she remained quiescent, hoping his passion would ignite some spark, that he would waken a genuine response. But as his breathing grew more harsh and uneven, and his mouth explored hers, she only became more detached and more ashamed of her own initiative. Finally she pulled away from him, struggling out of his imprisoning embrace.

Dave kept his hands on her forearms as she tried to move along the sofa. 'You asked for it,' he said.

'Yes, I know,' she admitted. 'I'm sorry.'

He took a couple of quick, rasping breaths, and said, 'Don't be. It's something to know that you *can* get carried away, sometimes. I thought you were——'

Astonished and a little wry, Cass looked up at him, and said, 'Frigid?'

'No. Just—a bit inhibited, maybe.' He shifted his grip to her hands and, lifting them up, kissed them. 'There's no need to be scared of me, you know. I wouldn't hurt you.'

'I'm not scared of you, Dave.'

'Good. Then let me kiss you again.'

He leaned over and touched her lips gently with his, then slid his hands up her arms to bring her closer, while the pressure of his mouth increased on hers. It was pleasant and sensuous and totally unexciting, and Cass was shocked at her own dispassionate attitude to his lovemaking. He carressed her back and shoulder and stroked her breast, and still she felt nothing but a mild pleasure in being held and touched. She had a disquieting conviction that if he had made love to her totally, the effect would have been just the same.

'I'm tired,' she murmured at last, making an excuse, partly to Dave and partly to herself.

'I'll take you to bed, if you like,' he muttered against her cheek.

Cass shook her head, and smiled. 'I'll go alone, thanks.'

He hadn't meant it, really. He knew she wouldn't . . .

His answering smile was resigned. 'Mm,' he said, his mouth lightly touching her nose, then her lips, and finally her forehead. He let her move out of his arms, but when she looked into his face there was something in his eyes she hadn't seen before. He raised his hand and touched her hair, and then her cheek. 'Cass,' he said, 'will you marry me?'

Her eyes widened a little.

Dave said, 'You can't be surprised. Haven't you been expecting it?'

'Not exactly. I know you said you love me, but it doesn't necessarily go with marriage these days.'

He smiled. 'Apparently it does, for you.'

'I—I don't know what to say.'

'You could say, "Mr Mercer, this is so sudden", but I'd prefer a simple, "Yes, please, Dave".'

She had to smile at his gentle humour. But she shook her head. 'I won't say either of them, if you don't mind.' She frowned slightly, looking perplexed.

'You haven't said no, anyway,' he reminded her after a moment. 'Does that mean the answer is "Maybe"?'

'I—suppose it does,' she told him. 'I'd like some time to think about it. But—thank you.'

'You've got it,' he said. 'But make up your mind in the next twenty years or so, won't you?'

He was grinning as he stood up, and Cass laughed

rather unsteadily. He was making it lighthearted and friendly, but his nice blue eyes were anxious, and the hand which smoothed his fair hair shook a little.

'I promise I will,' she said. 'One way or the other. It's a big decision.'

'I know. I sweated blood making up my mind to ask you.'

He was laughing, but he probably had. Dave had a pretty good life, no doubt he had put some thought into making such a drastic change in it as getting married. She ought to be pleased and flattered that he had asked her.

She *was*, of course. But she also had a nasty hollow feeling of trepidation in her stomach that didn't go away when he had left, but stayed with her long after she had gone to bed, and stopped her for hours from sleeping.

Next day she kept wondering why she hadn't just said yes. Dave was clever and funny and very nice, although she knew that somewhere in him there was a streak of determination that had carried him to prominence already in his chosen profession. He had told her that luck was responsible for his success, combined with a family background of involvement in the legal profession. But she had watched him in court on two occasions, when she had been preparing the article which had brought them together, and she had seen there a different person; he was cool and logical and incisive, and even his essential gentleness had been turned to the service of his profession. He never raised his voice or resorted to sarcasm, but she had seen one witness bewilderedly admitting under his soft but persistent questions that yes, he had said that, and yes, it did directly contradict what he had previously said, but . . .

And Dave had merely smiled understandingly and said quietly to the judge, 'Your Honour, I think the witness is a little confused. As you see, he really doesn't know what happened that day.'

She admired the man, didn't she? And liked him. And found his fair good looks very attractive, his gentle voice pleasant to the ear, his kisses not at all unwelcome . . .

So why shouldn't she marry him?

Because you don't love him, an insistent voice whispered.

Love—is that important? And how does one define love? she asked herself scornfully. I think I do love Dave.

You think! said the voice witheringly.

One was supposed to know, of course, irrevocably and without any doubt. Love, according to the books, hit one over the head and demanded recognition. One didn't have to hunt for clues to its presence. When it happened, it was unmistakable and overwhelming. But she didn't believe in books.

Well, Dave had given her time to think. Time to find that she did love him, perhaps. Certainly he was lovable enough. It shouldn't be difficult . . .

She thought about it constantly in the next couple of days. At the party they attended the next Saturday she thought about it, and the following day, as they drove out of the city and headed southward, then turned on to a quiet country road and looked out over bush-covered slopes to the farmlands, the city and the harbour drowsing beyond it.

Dave stopped the car at a lookout point where they could admire the view and drink in the tranquillity of quiet, rolling hills and the blue-hazed city and harbour.

He wound down the car window and Cass heard the muted purr of a car following the winding road, the persistent whisper of the wind in the darkness of the bush about them, and the intermittent calling of a bellbird somewhere within the trees.

His finger touched the slight frown between her fine brows. 'Hey,' he said, 'you've been looking tense all day. Is it me?'

Cass turned to him and smiled. 'Sort of. You've given me something to think about.'

'I hope so. Not to worry about, though. I never meant that. Relax and let it happen—okay?'

He leaned over to kiss her, and she met his lips with hers.

'Nice,' he said, as they parted again. 'Now, let's enjoy our day. I told you, I'm in no rush.'

She did manage to relax, and the next day she turned up at work feeling refreshed and ready for anything. Not quite ready, however, for the bombshell that descended on her.

Rudy poke his head out of his office almost as soon as she arrived, and barked, '*Cass!* I want you!'

As soon as she walked in, he said, 'You're doing the film thing, after all. And don't give me any excuses, Cass. Either you're a journo or you're not. You've got an assignment. Do it.'

'But you said that Pete——! He's been looking forward to it, too, Rudy. You can't——'

'Pete played football on Saturday, and he got a crack on the head and a back injury. He'll be in hospital for at least two weeks. The film crew arrives in New Zealand tomorrow. There's not a chance that anyone else could do it, so I'm assigning you. Any more questions?'

He glared at her, daring her to argue any further,

and she heaved a sigh and said, 'No. What do I do? Where do I find them?'

'They arrive this evening. Meet the plane. That way you're with them from the start, and if you can help them out in any way it'll maybe encourage them to co-operate when you want something from them. They're booked into a hotel for the night. Then they've got transport laid on, I believe, to take them up to the farm where they're filming. See if you can hitch a ride with them. I don't want you and Robby taking the firm's car for the whole week. We might need it here.'

'Supposing we need to come back for something?'

'Get a bus, hitch a ride—I dunno. Call us if you really have to, and I'll send someone to pick you up. You're supposed to live with the crew for the week— that's the object of the exercise. So don't make obstacles, huh? There's a good girl.'

Cass wasn't making obstacles, she was just asking practical questions. But it was no use arguing with Rudy in this mood. She left him chewing his lip and frowning ferociously as he picked up the phone to call a stringer who sometimes helped out in a part-time capacity, and went to find Robby.

Robby's real name was Ropata Kaimarama but, Ropata being the Maori form of Robert, everyone called him Robby. She found him fiddling a new film into one of the press cameras which were his pride and joy, and said, 'Have you heard? Pete's landed himself in hospital, and I've got to take his place for the Aussie film crew assignment.'

'I heard. Poor old Pete.' He grinned at her, and she wondered why toothpaste manufacturers didn't insist on always using Polynesian models for their advertisements. She was sure that teeth looked whiter in a brown face than a pasty pink one. 'So, it's you and me, eh, Cass?' Robby remarked. 'Well, you're a whole lot better looking than old Pete, anyway.'

Cass grinned back at the teasing twinkle in Robby's brown eyes. He was pretty good-looking himself, she thought dispassionately—tall and broad-shouldered, with regular features, and those dark eyes with their long lashes and fine black brows would have set any girl's heart mildly fluttering.

'You and me, mate,' she agreed solemnly. Her heart wasn't fluttering at all, but then she happened to know that although Robby was only her own age, he had been married for several years and had two lively little black-haired, brown-eyed boys as good-looking as himself.

'Does Susie mind you going away for a week?' she asked him.

'Not with Pete,' he answered cheerfully. 'Maybe I better not tell her it's you, after all.'

He didn't mean it. Susie and Cass were good friends, and Susie knew better than to be jealous of her husband's workmates. She also knew that Robby was immune to the occasional lures thrown his way by other girls. He had fallen in love with Susie when they were both at school, and never fallen out again. Cass laughed at him, and then sobered as he said, 'Rudy didn't tell me much about Pete, except that he's expected to be in hospital a couple of weeks. How bad is the back injury, do you know?'

'I phoned his wife. They reckon he'll be good as new, just about. Lorraine says she's not letting him play rugby again, though.'

'I'll bet! Well, we have to meet these film people. I suppose we can use the firm's car for that, but is there any chance of having yours for the rest of the week?'

'Nope. Sorry—Susie'll need it while I'm away.'

'Yes, of course. Oh, well, Rudy said hitch a ride with the film crew. I hope we can.'

This was all right, chatting about the details of the job, tidying up the loose ends. It kept her mind off the central problem of how she was going to manage meeting Lucien again.

Eventually, of course, it had to be faced. On the way out to the airport, she drove, determined to find something to concentrate on right up to the last minute. But as they turned into the long wide drive down to the terminal buildings, she felt the first flutter of apprehension in her throat. By the time she parked the car near the overseas terminal, her hands were slipping on the wheel with sweat, and her throat was dry.

Fortunately the flight was on time, and they didn't have too long to wait. They had asked for Mr Hale to be paged, and as she saw him break away from the group surrounding him and come towards the desk where she and Robby waited, Cass looked for the first sign of recognition in his face.

There was a fleeting flare of surprise before he took her hand, and she said, 'Mr Hale, I'm from *Citymag*——'

'I know,' he said, surprising her in turn. 'Hello, Cass.'

His hand gripped hers rather tightly, and when she made to withdraw it, it was a moment before his clasp loosened. She said, 'This is Robby Kaimarama, our photographer.'

Lucien shook Robby's hand, and smiled as he greeted him. She realised that he hadn't smiled at *her*.

'You're quick off the mark,' Lucien said, speaking to both of them.

'We thought we'd like to cover your arrival,' she explained. 'And also that there might be things we can help you with. If there's anything we can do . . .?'

She spoke formally, but Lucien smiled faintly and said, 'Kiwi hospitality—thanks, but I think everything's under control. We've got a special bus taking us and our gear to the hotel, and tomorrow it will move us out to the location.'

'Do you mind if we tag along, then? We'd like to meet the crew and perhaps get a few photographs.'

He shrugged indifferently. 'If you like. You've got your own transport, I take it?'

'At the moment, yes. Tomorrow, we may have to ask you for seats on the bus, if you can spare a couple.'

'I think that could be arranged. Come and meet the crew, then.'

They seemed a friendly lot, but Cass couldn't remember all the names, afterwards. She would have to get them down in her notebook tomorrow, she thought. The only ones who really stood out were the female lead, a stunning brunette whose name she had already heard—Odette Sullivan—and her screen partner, a tall, dark, and at the moment fiercely bearded man called Ethan Lyons.

Robby took some shots of them piling into the bus with their equipment, and then they followed the bus to the hotel. Some of the crew dumped their bags in their rooms and then willingly sat in one of the bars talking to Cass while she took notes on their various jobs, but Lucien didn't come down. He was, someone told her, on the phone, organising details. In time the gathering in the bar took on the atmosphere of a party, and eventually Cass put away her notebook and simply enjoyed herself.

There was an early start next morning. She hurriedly packed a bag before she went to bed, and was up before six so that she had plenty of time to make it to the hotel before seven-thirty, when the bus was due to depart with the film crew on board.

She dressed in neat pants and a cotton shirt, with a light jacket to ward off the morning chill, made herself a breakfast of egg on toast and coffee, and called a taxi before washing up.

The taxi arrived promptly, but when they were half way to the hotel, a car shot out of a side street in front of them, and the taxi slammed straight into its side.

For a few minutes there was chaos. Cass was flung against the back of the driver's seat, bruising her shoulder and, somehow, her knee. The driver's head thudded against the windscreen in spite of the seatbelt he wore, and he clapped a hand to his bruised forehead even as he cursed and unclipped his safety belt to fling out of the car and inspect the other vehicle, which was slewed across the road at right angles, its driver emerging white-faced and staggering from the passenger side, holding on to an arm which appeared to be broken.

By the time an ambulance arrived to take him to hospital, and a traffic officer had taken a statement from Cass as well as from the taxi driver, almost half an hour had elapsed. The driver radioed for another taxi for her, but she was nearly three-quarters of an hour late when she arrived at the hotel.

There was no sign of any bus, but Lucien was waiting at the entrance as she paid off the taxi and ran up the steps, with her bag bumping at her legs.

'I'm so so sorry;' she gasped. 'There was an accident——'

'You're not hurt?' he asked quickly.

'A bruise or two, that's all. Have you been waiting for me? The bus——?'

'I sent it on. You're coming with me.'

She looked confused, and he took her bag from her hand and said, 'I've hired an estate car. There's room for one passenger, along with the gear that's packed into it. Odette was supposed to be travelling with me, but she's gone with the rest. I said I'd wait for you.' He led the way to a dark red estate car parked at the kerb and pushed her bag in among a lot of mysterious bundles that occupied the luggage space. 'Robby seemed sure you'd be along eventually,' he added, opening the passenger door for her.

As he slid in beside her, she asked, 'Didn't *you* think I'd be along?' She wondered if he had thought she might have developed cold feet.

He glanced at her as he started the engine. 'I don't know you as well as Robby does, do I? Now, can you direct me by the best route out of the city? I haven't been in Auckland for some time, and it will save me consulting the map all the time.'

'Yes, of course.' She gave him the directions calmly, taking them quickly out of the city streets on to the motorway which cut across Auckland, over the Harbour Bridge to the North Shore, and out to the main northern highway.

The pretty North Shore suburbs, filled with trees on hillsides above the harbour, gave way to the rolling farmlands of Albany and Silverdale, with their roadside fruit and vegetable shops, and occasional signs offering pottery or craft goods for sale.

They had been driving for some time in silence when Lucien said, 'You won't be popular with Odette. She didn't want to go in the bus.'

'Well, I'm sorry. I didn't plan the accident.' Cass

wondered if the actress thought it beneath her dignity to travel by bus, or if she had a personal reason for wanting to be Lucien's passenger. She cast a quick glance at him, wondering if he was disappointed, too. Odette was a beautiful woman, and Lucien wasn't immune to a pretty face.

He looked down and their eyes clashed for a moment. She read curiosity in his before he remarked, returning his gaze to the road, 'You've changed.'

For a moment she was disconcerted. It had been almost as if they had never met, and she had wondered if that was the way he was going to play it. If so, it suited her. She didn't want to be reminded of their previous acquaintance at all. But she supposed it was rather silly to ignore altogether the fact that they had met before. The thing was to be sensible about it, casual and calm. 'Have I?' she said, with admirable cool. 'How?'

Lucien looked at her again briefly. 'I'm not sure. It's been nearly two years, hasn't it?'

She shrugged. 'Yes, it must be. I suppose I've grown up.'

'*Weren't* you grown up, then? You were all of twenty-one, as I remember.'

'And a bit,' she confirmed. 'I was a late developer. I think I was still adolescent, then.'

This time his quick glance was sharp and calculating. She had a feeling he was reading all sorts of things into that remark that she hadn't meant at all, and she hastened to steer the conversation into less dangerous waters. 'You didn't seem very surprised to see me,' she said.

'I wasn't. I knew that you worked for *Citymag*.'

'Did you?' She voiced her blank surprise.

'Your editor sent me copies of the magazine when

he asked if I would agree to having a reporter do a story on the filming. Your name is on the masthead.'

She couldn't resist saying it. 'So you had to believe, at last, that I really am a journalist?' she asked dryly.

'Oh, I knew you were a journalist,' he said casually. 'I checked your story with Hal, before we left the ship.'

CHAPTER SEVEN

CASS sat there feeling numb with shock. Lucien had known before the ship docked that she had been telling the truth about Hal, that she was a journalist doing her job, not a cheap opportunist willing to sell herself for a slice of Hal's money. And he had done nothing about it. It apparently hadn't been that important to him.

She thought back to the traumatic few minutes he had put her through, and was suddenly burningly angry. Tightly, she said, 'Then don't you think you owe me an apology?'

He didn't look at her as he asked carelessly, 'What for?'

Cass was speechless. He hadn't *forgotten*, had he? He *couldn't* have! Finally, she said in icy tones, 'For making false accusations, for a start!'

'Like what?'

'Like saying that I was willing to—to sleep with Hal because of his money!'

He shrugged. 'It amounts to the same thing, doesn't it?'

'What on earth is *that* supposed to mean?'

'Money—a story—whatever you wanted.'

'I don't know what you're getting at. I was doing my *job*!'

Lucien suddenly swung the wheel, turning the car into a side road, rough-surfaced and narrow, winding up a hillside into dusty bush that hid the main road when he drew on to the grass verge and twisted to face her. 'You do put a lot of yourself into your job, don't you?' he asked her jeeringly, his eyes light and hard. 'You'd do anything for a story!'

She looked back at him in bewilderment. If he had spoken to Hal, then he knew she hadn't slept with the man. What *was* he on about?

Then he said, 'I remember when you thought *I* was your target. You played me so cleverly—dangling your pretty self before my eyes, advancing, retreating. What a pity I missed out on the final stages of the campaign, when you found out your mistake. I'd love to know what you'd planned . . .'

'It wasn't like that!' she protested.

He raised his brows sceptically, and she said, 'I know I engineered that first meeting, and yes, I thought you were Lionel Halliday. I shouldn't have done it, I admit it was—underhand. But I could have lost my job if I hadn't got that interview, and Rudy had told me he hated publicity. It just seemed a good idea to get to know him first, and bring up the idea later when—when——'

'When you'd charmed him into a more receptive frame of mind. Only you picked on the wrong man, for a start. All the same, I must congratulate you on not wasting any time once you found out your mistake. You must have found Hal an easy mark, after all.'

'I was lucky. Patsy——'

'Oh, yes, Patsy. A very obliging girl.'

'Yes, she was, actually.'

'I heard.' His face was rigid with distaste. 'She spent the afternoon in the lounge bar with Tony. Why are you looking surprised? Don't you remember the ship had a very efficient grapevine?'

What did that have to do with anything? Cass wondered. Then, suspicion beginning to stir in her mind, she said slowly, 'What did Hal say to you?'

'You really want to know?' His mouth sneered, and she looked away, but said stubbornly, 'Yes.'

'He said,' Lucien told her with deliberation, 'that he didn't normally give interviews, but when a girl had as much to offer as you had, he was willing to make an exception. He seemed well pleased with the arrangement.'

She could hear Hal's leer in Lucien's voice. She felt sick. Not wanting to admit that he had made a pass and been turned down, the man had boasted instead of a non-existent conquest. And Lucien had believed him.

She was shaking with anger, her hands clenched in her lap. She should tell him that it wasn't true, but when she tried to open her lips and say so, they trembled too much, and she closed her mouth again firmly. Was it likely, anyway, that he would believe her now, when he hadn't before? Hal had only confirmed what he had already thought was the truth.

Lucien began, 'Cass——' and reached for her, his hands digging into her shoulders, his fingers hurting the bruised one so that she let out a small shriek of pain, her face contorted and white.

His hands fell away immediately, his voice sharp as he demanded, 'What's the matter?'

'My shoulder!' she gasped, her hand covering the spot, outside her shirt. 'It got a bang this morning. It's bruised.'

'Are you sure it's only a bruise? Let me see.'

His hands went to the button on her shirt, and she knocked them away violently, retreating from him against the door. 'Don't touch me!'

'I'm sorry. There's no need to act like a Sabine maiden. I wasn't going to ravish you.'

He sounded amused, and she felt silly. 'I didn't imagine you were.' she said coolly. 'But I'm sure it's only a bruise, and I don't want it touched. Shouldn't we be getting on?'

She wouldn't look at him, and after a moment he said flatly, 'Yes.'

He restarted the engine, and she breathed a quiet sigh of relief as he turned the car to the main road.

They breasted the hill at Orewa and ran down across the concrete bridge and past the long sweep of the beach almost hidden by the homes built along the shore. Then they were travelling uphill again, the road curving down the other side to the small settlement at Waiwera, where the attraction for holidaymakers and day visitors was not so much the small sheltered beach, as the hot springs which fed a popular swimming pool. As he changed gear for another steep, winding slope, Lucien said, 'You've certainly no shortage of hills here.'

'Blame the brothers of Maui,' Cass advised him flippantly.

'I don't get the connection. Maui's the Maori hero who harnessed the sun, isn't he?'

'He also fished up the North Island from the sea. It's called The Fish of Maui. He left his brothers to guard it, and while he was away they began carving bits off it for themselves. That's why it's so uneven and hilly.'

Lucien laughed. 'I'll believe it. Did you know that Maui turns up in mythology all over the Pacific?'

'No. I thought he was a Maori legend. But then I suppose the early Maoris, wherever they came from originally, brought their mythology with them.'

'I guess,' he said absently. 'We must have to turn

off here somewhere.' He looked down as they traversed
a ridge, with a steep valley falling away on each side.
The views were breathtaking, the valleys holding shallow sweeps of water, and the sea beyond a narrow shelf
of land on the right was a brilliant summer blue.

'What are we looking for?' Cass asked, as he slowed
and peered at a name on a rural delivery letterbox at
the roadside.

'A white-painted wooden gate and the name
Burnsdale,' he told her. 'Ah, here we are.'

She climbed out to open the gate for him, rather
glad to leave the car for a few minutes. On the surface
they were being civilised and even friendly, two old
acquaintances sharing a journey. But she felt tense and
aware of his every movement, and she could see the
whiteness of his knuckles which meant he was gripping
the steering wheel much more tightly than he needed
to. There was an atmosphere in the car that was almost
tangible. Even laughing together hadn't dispelled it.

They drove down the hill and through trees, and
eventually emerged on flat ground at nearly sea level.
Hidden from the road was a sprawling farmhouse with
a dozen small cabins not far from it. The bus was there,
and there was a lot of activity going on.

Robby came up as they climbed out of the car, and
Cass explained about the accident that had delayed her.
Lucien was consulting with the young woman who
Cass remembered had been introduced as his secretary,
and after a few minutes he turned to Cass and asked,
'Will you mind sharing a cabin with one of the other
girls?'

'Of course not,' she said. 'I half expected we'd be in
tents. Rudy said the place was run as a private motor
camp, normally. When he told me you'd said accom-
modation could be arranged for us, I didn't expect it

to be five-star, exactly.'

The secretary smiled at her and said, 'I've put you in with me, if that's okay?'

'Fine. Can I take my bag there now?'

She wanted to get away from Lucien. Even now, while he looked around the site, apparently ignoring her, she was conscious of him standing there not three feet away. His very presence seemed overwhelming. She didn't think she could have stood another minute of being in the car with him.

The secretary showed her the way, saying, 'My name's Barbara Kaye. I don't suppose you can remember all the names from yesterday.'

She was right. Cass recalled the first names of most of those who had been in the hotel bar, but neither Barbara nor her boss had been present. Presumably he had needed her assistance.

The cabin was neat and clean though not luxurious, and it had its own spartan but clean bathroom facilities.

'The stars have their own caravans,' Barbara explained without rancour, 'and Lucien has one which doubles as his office. The rest of us muck in together— well, in pairs, anyway.'

'Will you have time to give me an interview?' Cass asked, thinking that the director's secretary would be a useful contact and source of information.

'Depends on Lucien,' said Barbara. 'He keeps me pretty busy as a rule, and of course anything I said would have to be cleared with him.'

'Of course.' Cass tried to sound noncommittal, but Barbara cast her a sharp glance before she turned away, saying, 'Settle yourself in. I'll see you later. Lunch is on the verandah of the house, by the way, in fine weather. If it rains we all crowd into the dining room.'

Be careful, Cass told herself as she combed her hair and gave her lipstick a quick touch-up. Better keep on the right side of Barbara. She seemed a friendly type, as well as efficient. She looked thirtyish, and was attractive in a totally unstartling way, brown-haired and brown-eyed, with a nice smile and freckles running across the bridge of a pert nose.

Cass unpacked and hung up a few clothes, and then took her notebook and small tape recorder outside.

There was still a lot of activity, but now it seemed to have acquired a more organised and purposeful flavour. The boss-man had arrived, Cass thought wryly, and there he was in the centre of it, with Barbara at his elbow. Everything was revolving about him. He would call and point, and someone jumped to it, and every so often someone came up to consult with him, and went off again with an air of knowing now exactly what to do.

She could have sworn he hadn't looked in her direction, but suddenly Barbara left his side and came over to her, handing her a folder of papers. 'The script,' she explained. 'Lucien said to give you a copy.'

'Thanks. Where is he off to, now?' He was striding away with another man, and Cass didn't want to miss anything.

'Down to the beach to discuss this afternoon's filming.'

'Then I'm going, too.' She looked about for Robby and beckoned to him. Barbara looked doubtful, but said nothing as she turned away to the call of one of the other crew members.

Cass and Robby hurried after the two men. The sea could just be glimpsed beyond patches of thick bush, between a couple of steep sandhills covered with marram grass and cat-tails. A shallow creek ran between the hills, and down across the white sand to the waves' edge. When she and Robby emerged on to the beach, they saw that it was long and curved, with occasional groups of black boulders rising from the sand, and a long rocky shelf running into the sea at one end, with blood-red pohutukawas clinging to the cliff face behind it, the dropped blossoms littering the shelf.

Lucien and the other man had stopped and were conferring, looking about them. They turned as Cass and Robby approached, and Cass asked, 'Mind if we listen in?'

For a moment she fancied that Lucien's eyes were hostile. Then they became merely indifferent, and he said, without smiling, 'Please yourselves. It's only a technical discussion.'

From then on he ignored them, although they trailed behind when he and the cameraman moved over to the rock shelf, talking about camera angles and backlighting. Most of it made little sense to Cass, but Robby's eyes gleamed with interest. He took one picture as Lucien made a sweeping gesture with his hands, explained how he wanted a particular shot to be framed, and the other man stood watching intently. Then it was apparently over, and as they walked back to the gap in the hills, Robby buttonholed the cameraman, who seemed happy to be able to talk with a fellow-enthusiast.

Cass found herself walking beside Lucien, the other two dropping behind, deep in discussion.

'Was that useful?' Lucien asked her abruptly.

'I don't know yet. I might get a sentence out of it. Or just a caption for that picture that Robby took. Thank you for the script.'

'It might save some unnecessary questions.'

She deduced that he meant it would save him or his

crew time in answering unnecessary questions. 'Well, thanks anyway,' she murmured dryly.

He glanced at her sharply. 'You can ask anyone anything you like,' he said. 'Only I want to see your copy before you send it in.'

'We don't accept censorship,' she warned him.

'Who said anything about censorship? We've got nothing to hide. I just don't want the whole plot line of the film given away, or any inaccurate statements made.'

'I don't make inaccurate statements,' Cass said coldly.

'Don't be so touchy. Even the best of journalists make mistakes. It could save you some embarrassment.'

'I *am* the best,' she retorted, firing up. 'And I always check my facts.'

'Yeah, at first hand—I remember,' he jeered softly. 'I still want to see your copy.'

She would have shown it to him anyway, as a matter of courtesy, though Rudy would have the final say on what went into the magazine and what didn't. But that little taunt had been quite gratuitous. She said, 'If *you* were a journalist, you might have checked some facts yourself.'

'I did,' he reminded her.

He had talked to Hal, and Hal had lied—by implication, perhaps, but lied all the same. *Men*, she thought bitterly. They were all alike. A woman scorned was nothing compared to a man who had been turned down by a woman he wanted. Or one who thought he had been used by a woman.

Lunch was served soon after they got back. It was buffet style salads and cold meats, and people perched on the verandah rails or sat on the steps or the grass to eat. All excepting the dark-haired female lead, Odette Sullivan, who was given a chair and sat in a corner of the verandah while Lucien leaned on the rail nearby and talked to her.

In the afternoon the whole company trooped down to the beach and some scenes were run through, but there was no actual filming. Cass made numerous notes, carefully keeping out of the way, and Robby, who had made a friend of the cameraman, happily snapped several pictures.

The evening meal was served inside, in a large dining room into which three long tables had been crammed. Odette and Lucien were both missing, and she gathered that they were eating together in the star's caravan. Going over the script, someone said. Ethan Lyons ate with one hand and ignored everyone as he studied the script he held in the other.

Cass read her own copy afterwards, lying on her bed in the small cabin, her shoulders propped against pillows. The story was historical, and concerned a small band of convicts who had escaped from the penal colony of New South Wales in the early eighteen-thirties, and commandeered a ship in Sydney Harbour which they sailed to New Zealand. There were seven men and two women in the party at the beginning, but one of the women, who had been injured in the escape, died at sea. Odette played the other woman, arriving in a strange, primitive and hostile land with a group of hardened criminals, all of them knowing that if they were ever caught and sent back to Australia, they would almost certainly hang. It was a gripping story with plenty of action as tension mounted among the group, and they coped with the problems of survival in a strange environment, and the realisation that there could be no going back. The advent of a Maori war party into their lives added further complications to the plot, and Cass found herself wondering with growing excitement if the finished film would do justice to the story.

Shooting began early in the morning, and for the first time, Cass saw the actors in make-up and costume. It was fascinating to see that Odette had been made to look haggard and exhausted, her beauty dimmed as she played out a scene which took place shortly after the convicts' arrival on the shore, where they pessimistically discussed their future.

Cass thought the first take went well, but Lucien made them do it over and over, until he was satisfied with every detail, every nuance of speech. He was patient and implacable, and she found herself in the end watching him rather than the actors, looking for the faint nod of approval, the slight tightening of his mouth and quick frown when he was dissatisfied.

Once he caught her eye, but his gaze was unseeing, and she realised that he hadn't noticed her at all. His whole attention was on the scene being acted out in front of the cameras. At the moment it was the only thing that mattered to him.

In the next few days she came to respect that total dedication of his, as she saw that his crew did. He could be bitingly sarcastic about sloppy work, and grimly impatient with what he saw as stupidity, but he got results, and the people who worked with him knew that he would tolerate nothing short of perfection. Those who cared about what they were doing—and Cass soon realised as she talked to them that the majority of the crew did care very deeply—gave him top marks for keeping them all on their toes. They wanted the film to be a success, and they knew that Lucien would ensure that it was.

At the end of four days, she had filled three note-books, and used four tapes. She knew that the main problem with the story was going to be deciding what could be left out. But although she had interviewed several key members of the crew, she had not found an opportunity to speak to either Odette or Lucien alone. When they were not filming or asleep, they seemed to be invariably sitting apart, their heads close as they talked, or else they had disappeared together.

The general consensus was that they were having an affair, and Cass had no reason to dispute it. Watching them together irritated her, and she told herself it was because she needed to talk to them both, and there never seemed to be a chance.

At last she decided to take the bull by the horns. After they had eaten that evening, she walked over to where they were sitting in a corner of the verandah, and addressed Odette. 'I wonder if you could spare me the time for an interview?' she asked pleasantly. 'I would like to have your views on the film and especially on your own part, for the article I'm writing.'

The actress made a little grimace. 'Now?' she said, giving a sidelong glance at Lucien, as though she couldn't bear to be parted from him.

'Whenever it suits you,' Cass told her. 'But I only have another day here. I would be grateful . . .'

Lucien said, 'Might as well get it over with, Odette. It's publicity, remember.'

He got up and walked away, and Odette pouted at his oblivious back and shrugged, 'The great man has spoken. Let's go to my caravan, then, and you can tell me what you want to know.'

It started slowly, as she retold in rather bored tones how she had acted in school plays, then theatre and television, with a stint in Britain, and returned to

Australia for the starring role in this film. But when she began to talk about the character she was portraying, Cass began to realise that she was listening to a thorough professional.

'I see her as developing throughout the story,' Odette said, her hands moving in a widening gesture to illustrate her point. 'She's survived up until now by clinging to men, the only way she knows. She's the only woman, and she's married to the oldest of the convicts, but she doesn't love him. It was better to be married, for a woman in her circumstances, so she took the first chance that came along.'

'That isn't in the script, is it?' Cass asked.

'It's how I see it. That's why she's attracted to Denning, the leader. Not just because he's young and handsome, which Ethan *is*, of course, but because he's the strong one, the one she feels safe with. She's here alone with this gang of men, and she knows she's in constant danger of rape, and that Wilson isn't strong enough to protect her. That's why she starts eyeing young Denning.'

'Fear?' Cass asked quickly. 'Not sex?'

Odette's eyes sparkled with something like laughter. 'Oh, you're fast!' she said. 'But then you're a woman. Lucien kept harping on the fact that the woman had an eye for the main chance. He wanted me to play it like that—a sort of female Machiavelli.'

'But you're not going to? You want to make her a more sympathetic character?' Cass felt an excitement of her own. This was getting interesting. She checked that the tape was rolling, and glanced back at Odette.

The other girl was looking thoughtful. 'Well, I haven't convinced him yet, but he said the concept was interesting. Which means he'll think about it.'

'Supposing he doesn't agree with you?'

Odette grimaced. 'He's the director. I'll have to play it his way.'

'What about when Denning hands you over to the local Maori chief? In the script it reads as though the poor girl is terrified. Lucien can't see the woman planning *that*, surely?'

'No, but he pointed out that as soon as she realises she's not destined for the oven, after all, she pulls herself together and starts plotting her revenge on Denning.'

'Yes, and of course she uses the chief as her instrument of revenge, egging him on to attack the convicts. I can see Lucien's point.'

'So can I. But I think this is the turning point, where she finally realises that she can't rely on any man to protect her, that she has to be strong herself.'

'And so she kills the chief, when he comes back with Denning's head?'

'Yes, not in grief and remorse, but because she's decided at last to take charge of her own destiny, and not rely on the strength of a man—any man.'

'That sounds like a feminist point of view. Do you think you can convince the director?'

'I'm trying. Lucien isn't a male chauvinist, you know. He's just a little soured by experience.'

'What do you mean?' Cass felt a quickening of interest.

'Off the record?' said Odette, glancing at the recorder.

Cass reached for the off switch and the tape stilled. She looked up expectantly, and saw Odette chewing her lip. She waited.

'I shouldn't, I suppose,' Odette mused. 'He'd kill me.'

'Off the record. I promise.'

'I like you,' Odette said unexpectedly. 'I suppose most people do; that's how you get them to talk, isn't it?'

Cass still said nothing. It was a technique she had learned, and it usually worked. It did now.

Odette gave a little laugh, and said, 'If you ever breathe a word——! Well, Lucien and I worked together in England once or twice. There was a girl he was smitten with—I mean, head over heels. She was ambitious and apparently he was only a stepping stone. Lucien introduced her to an important producer, and she stepped on to him. Lucien was shattered. My husband and I sort of helped him pick up the pieces. He's had a warped view of women ever since, I think. He's dead suspicious and, although he denies it, he's inclined to take the worst interpretation of a woman's behaviour. That's why he's reluctant to accept my view of this film.'

Cass didn't comment. She said, 'I didn't know you were married,' and with a glance asked permission to switch on the recorder, her finger on the button.

Odette nodded, and explained, 'I'm not, any more. My fault, I guess. I was spending a lot of time on my career, and somehow we woke up one day and found there was nothing left.' She shrugged. 'Well, he's married again, and I've got my work.'

'You've given up a lot for your career. You must be very dedicated.'

'You make me sound like Pavlova! I would say I'm absorbed in it. Almost literally, when I'm working on a film. I like to steep myself in the part, and just think about it. I know the script backwards. Having a lead role has one great advantage, in my view—I can demand privacy and get it. I find being with other people distracting. I guess they think I'm standoffish, but I want to give my best to this role. It's important. I want to turn in the best performance of my career. It's a good script and we've got a fine director, and I'd like to do them both justice. Apart from the fact that of course it would be good for me professionally.'

'May I quote that?' Cass asked.

Odette shrugged. 'If you like. Did I sound pompous?'

'Not at all. Is that why you weren't keen to give me an interview? I've interfered with your steeping yourself in the part?'

'Oh—sorry. Was I rude?' Her blue eyes were rueful.

'Not rude, just obviously reluctant. I think I've got enough, anyway, unless there's anything you'd specially like to add?'

Odette shook her head, and Cass gathered her recorder and notebook up and said, 'I'll leave you to it, then. Sorry if I broke your concentration.'

'It's okay. I guess you're "dedicated" too, aren't you? Lucien said something of the sort.'

'Did he?' Cass hesitated, but Odette didn't volunteer any further information, and Cass wasn't going to ask for it. He had probably said it with a sneer. Well, it didn't matter. One more day and they need never see each other again.

The thought brought a peculiar little ache to her chest that she irritably tried to quell.

CHAPTER EIGHT

LUCIEN was now here in sight when Cass emerged from Odette's caravan. She wandered over to the cabin she shared with Barbara, who was pulling on a pair of jeans over a brief bikini. 'Hi,' she smiled. 'Some of us are going for a swim. Like to come?'

It would be starting to get dark soon, but the day had been hot and sticky, and the thought of a cool swim was tempting. Cass put away her notebook and tape recorder and rummaged for her own swimsuit, threw a towelling shift on over the white satin bits of nothing, and joined Barbara and the dozen or so others who were heading for the beach.

The sun was sending a pale shimmer over the water, which looked lazy and inviting, long, low, sweeping waves unfolding themselves gently on to the beach. The sand was still warm under their feet, and the rock outcrop further along the beach had a mysterious, brooding quality, black and glistening in the fading sunlight. They had been filming along there today, doing a sequence where the convicts, desperate for food, fossicked around the rock pools for sea-eggs and mussels, and tried to catch crabs in the pools, while the water broke against the rocks and soaked them again and again. Odette soon had damp hair straggling about her shoulders, and her thin dress clung to her figure as she grimly tore at the black-shelled mussels along with the others. It had been a cleverly handled sequence, with the men at first concentrating on nothing but the food they were able to wrest from the sea and the rocks, and then, as they gradually began to feed their hunger and feel it less fiercely, first one and then another would cast a sidelong glance at the girl in their midst, until she finally looked up and found them all gazing at her with unmistakable awareness of her sex. When Lucien had finally called, 'Cut!' Cass had found her own palms damp with tension, and she breathed a sigh of relief as the men relaxed and turned back into the nice, normal members of the cast that she had come to know.

Odette seemed to take a little longer to unwind. She stayed where she was with the water tugging at her long skirt, and her head bent, until Lucien went over to her with a blanket in his hand and, pulling her up on to the rock shelf, put it round her shoulders, keeping his arm round her while he led her to a sheltered spot and sat her down on the great twisted root of one of the pohutukawas. After a while she pushed the wet hair from her eyes and smiled at him, and he left her, to talk to one of the men.

The rocks were deserted, now, as Cass pulled off her shift and went into the water with Barbara. The first shock was cold, but the sun had been blazing all day, and the water still held its warmth. She swam lazily, remembering the way Lucien had looked down at Odette, his mouth gentle and his eyes concerned. They suited each other, she supposed. Odette was as singleminded as he was about the film. Everyone thought they were lovers, and everyone was probably right. It was none of Cass's business, anyway.

She turned on her back, floating, and watching the sky. It was paling, losing its blue intensity, and a tiny star flickered weakly above her already. As the sky darkened again to indigo, more stars pricked their way through the deepening haze, and dusk mantled the trees edging the sand.

She swam slowly back to the beach, and, as she stood with the waves pulling at her thighs, discovered Lucien standing watching her from the water's edge. He had evidently been swimming, too. His hair was sleek and darkened with water, and his body glistened with it. He put out his hand to her as she came out of the water, and took hers. There were only two or three of the others left, drying themselves and making back to the camp to change. She must have stayed in a long time, longer than she had realised.

She broke away from Lucien and picked up her shift, lifting it over her head and pulling it on over her wet body. It clung in places, and she caught Lucien's eyes as he stood watching her. A shock jolted through her, because the look in his eyes was disturbingly like the looks that the men in the cast had given to Odette on camera that afternoon.

'I want to talk to you,' he said. 'Come along to my office.'

Cass shrugged, and walked alongside him. He had slung a towel about his shoulders, and rubbed his wet hair with one end of it as they walked. 'Hadn't we better change first?' she suggested.

Lucien looked at her, making her flush, and drawled, 'Maybe you'd better.'

She hoped he would, too, she thought, as she stripped off her wet things and pulled on a brief sleeveless top and cotton skirt. She found him too profoundly male in nothing but swim shorts that barely covered his hips.

When she knocked on his door, he opened it wearing a denim shirt that he hadn't bothered to button up, and pair of shabby jeans. It was what he wore most of the time on the set, but he wasn't usually this close.

His maleness still bothered her. She told herself not to be silly, and stepped inside at his silent invitation.

The small table at one end was covered with papers, some with diagrams on them, some typed. There were papers on the divan beds flanking it, too, but Lucien scooped most of them off one and told her to sit down. He leaned on the table and folded his arms, looking down at her.

'Odette's been telling you we've a difference of opinion about how her role should be played,' he said.

'Yes.'

'You're not to print any of that.'

Annoyed, Cass said, 'Why not? Aren't differences of opinion allowed in your cast?'

'They're not for publication. I don't want the public confused before they've even seen the film.'

'I won't confuse them. Odette's views were interesting, and what she had to say gives an insight into how she goes about playing a part. It was one of the best interviews I've done.'

'Some of my best work ends up on the cutting room floor.'

'And some of mine in the wastebasket, but it's because I decided to rewrite, or the editor cuts it, not because an outsider wants to dictate what's printed and what isn't.'

'I'm not an outsider. You're here with my permission, and there are some areas of information which are—privileged, if you like. Definitely off the record.'

'This wasn't one of them, as far as Odette was concerned.'

'Look, I'm trying to save you from writing it and then seeing it cut out, either when I vet the article or when it's edited. If I have to, I'll go over your head, you stubborn little mule.'

'There's no need to call me names! Why couldn't you have just asked me nicely to leave it out, instead of giving me orders? Your cast and crew may have to put up with you acting like a petty despot. *I* don't work for you!'

She got up off the divan, to stand facing him, her eyes flashing with temper.

'I'm not asking for favours,' Lucien told her. 'There's no point in saying "pretty please", when you're not at liberty to refuse.'

'It's more polite!'

'It's hypocritical. However, you're right about calling you names. I apologise—though I could think of worse things . . .'

Cass looked indignant, then found him giving her a teasing grin, his eyes alight with humour. Caught unawares, she found her own mouth curling up with laughter. She bit her lip, but it was too late, and Lucien took her arm, firmly pushing he back on to the divan, and said, 'Sit down, I'll pour you a drink.'

He gave her gin and tonic, and sat down beside her with a glass in his own hand. He touched it to hers, and said, 'It's been a long time, Cass.'

'Yes.' Soberly, she looked down at her drink, feeling suddenly depressed. He sipped at his drink, watching her, and said quietly, 'Drink up.'

She raised the glass to her lips. He had made it just the way she liked it, and she realised he hadn't asked what she wanted. He had remembered her taste, and assumed she hadn't changed in that respect.

He asked, 'How is the article going?'

'The only problem is what I'm going to leave out.'

'You should be grateful to me, then.'

'I'd rather leave out something else. Does it matter

so much, if the public knows there were differing points of view?'

'Yes, because we can only play it one way, and I don't want the patrons and the critics sitting through it wondering how it would have been if we'd played the other way. Odette tells me you agreed with her version. Were you being diplomatic, or simply scoring a point off me?'

'There is a third possibility,' Cass pointed out.

'Yes, that you genuinely think her way is better. Do you?'

'Actually, yes. It's more believable to me.' Cass looked at him thoughtfully. 'Ruth *is* a woman. Don't you think you should accept a woman's point of view on the character and her motivations?'

'Maybe. But don't some women deceive themselves about their motives?'

'Don't men?' she countered.

Lucien smiled, finished his drink and placed the glass on the table among the papers, leaning across her. 'Maybe.' He sat back, folded his arms and regarded her steadily. 'Odette is convinced she has me taped. Maybe a man is better able to judge a woman's motives. Looking in from outside, so to speak.'

'No,' she said. '*You* don't understand how Odette— how *Ruth* felt—in that scene this afternoon.'

His eyes narrowed suddenly with concentration. 'That flash of panic,' he said, 'just before I cut the scene. It seemed—real. It shook me.'

Cass looked at the quarter inch of liquid left in her glass. She heard him say deliberately, 'I'd seen that look once before on a woman's face—yours.'

The glass in her hand shook, and she put it down beside his and clenched her hands together to stop them trembling.

Lucien said, '*Are* women that scared—of men?'

She looked up at him fleetingly and realised that he was thinking of his film. His face was intent, as she had seen it when he watched the scene this afternoon, before the climactic moment when Odette, as Ruth, looked up and found the men's eyes devouring her body. He wanted to know because it was important for what he was doing in the film, not because he was concerned with what Odette had really felt, or what Cass had felt two years ago.

For a moment she was blindly furious, and shaking with a need to hit him and run. But his very lack of emotion steadied her, and she managed to answer evenly, with only a little huskiness in her voice, 'Yes, they are. When they think they have reason.'

'What's a reason?' he asked, almost impatiently. 'A look? A threatening word? A kiss that's less than gentle?'

'*Yes*. Yes, sometimes that's enough—because you only have to lay hands on a woman to prove how strong you are. And every woman in her bones knows that if a man is determined on rape, nothing is going to stop him. Nothing that *she* can do, on her own.'

'That's not a very liberated view.'

'It's a realistic view.'

'Then you must walk around in a constant state of fear,' he said slowly, as though he didn't believe it.

'Not fear,' she said. 'That would be paranoid. No one can live like that. But—wariness, yes—I suppose we all have that. It's a basic tenet of self-preservation, for women. It's always there, just below the surface.'

'But for God's sake! All men aren't rapists!'

'How do we know?' she asked quietly. 'I wouldn't have picked you, until——'

He was silent, frowning. Then he said, 'I wouldn't have raped you.'

'No?' Cass let irony colour her tone. She stood up, and Lucien came to his feet, too, his eyes angry, darkly grey.

He made a quick, impatient movement, half turning from her. 'Perhaps, of a virgin, I might believe it,' he said. 'But women like you and Odette——' He turned back to her and his eyes raked her, hard and sceptical.

Anger flared in her. 'You believe what you want to,' she said. 'You saw Odette's face.'

'She's an actress!'

'Oh, sure! You know that wasn't just acting. But then you wouldn't know a fact if it hit you in the face. You're so full of male prejudice that you can't see what's right in front of your eyes. So make the film your way, if you like. It won't be so authentic, but men will like it. They might even manage to believe in it.'

'Hang on, there!' he ordered as she turned to leave. His hand clamped on her arm and swung her round to face him. 'Just hang on,' he repeated.

Her head went up and she tried to pull back from him, to jerk her arm from his hold. His other hand came up and he held her shoulders and pulled her close, and as her hands automatically flattened against his chest she felt the hard bone and muscle under her palms, the warmth of his thighs against hers, his breath on her face. A flare of desire shot through her body. She trembled, and saw his eyes narrow suddenly.

He said softly, knowingly, 'You're not afraid of me.'

For a moment longer he stayed staring down at her, and there was calculation in the glinting grey of his eyes. Then he lowered his head and kissed her.

As his lips met hers and firmly parted them, Cass

made a small sound of denial and tried to push against him. But he only shifted his hold, one hand going behind her head, his fingers tangling in her hair, and the other behind her, bringing her even closer to his body.

She couldn't escape, but the worst of it was that she knew she didn't want to. His mouth was warm and inviting, and the hard masculinity against the length of her body was infinitely exciting, making her long to arch against him and hold him as he was holding her. Her hands moved convulsively, and she curled them tightly to stop herself from sliding them up round his neck. With despair she realised that nothing had changed. Lucien could still make her want him as no other man had, before or since she had met him.

His mouth was coaxing hers, moving over her lips until she felt a dizzying sense of pleasure, and her lips involuntarily opened further to his passionate exploration. He began to kiss her deeply, and his hand moved from behind her head and caressed her shoulder and back. He touched her breast, and she drew a shuddering breath and at last dredged up the willpower to wrench her mouth from his and say hoarsely, 'No!'

She was straining against his arms, but he let her move only an inch or two, still easily holding her. She said, 'Let me go,' and her fists pushed against his shoulders, her eyes avoiding his.

'Why?' he asked. 'You want me, too.'

Cass shook her head. 'No.'

'Liar. You responded to me just now.'

'It was only a kiss. That doesn't mean I want to sleep with you.'

'What's the matter? Do you only give yourself when you know you'll get a story in return?'

She stared at him, and then anger gave her the

strength to wrest herself away from him. 'You swine!' she snapped. 'What about you?'

'*What* about me?'

Her head was flung back in challenge. 'Do you think I don't know why you kissed me? That wasn't love-making, that was an experiment—you were testing a theory for your precious film!'

Something in his face changed subtly. He looked very mocking, his hands thrust into his pockets. 'Well,' he drawled, 'the results were certainly interesting.'

She badly wanted to slap him. She clenched her hands at her side to stop herself from doing it, and turned, making for the door. As she wrenched it open, Lucien said from behind her, 'You've forgotten something, haven't you?'

'What do you mean?'

'Don't you need an interview with me?'

She did, of course. It was something she had meant to bring up, when he had told her to come here tonight. She wanted to fling out, tell him she would do without it, thanks, that she could do without seeing *him*, ever again. But professionalism got in the way. Of course the article wouldn't be complete without interviewing the director, he was the man who made it all happen. She swallowed her pride and said stiffly, 'Yes. When would it suit you?'

She was standing with her hand on the door, holding it half open. Lucien strolled over and leaned against the jamb, his arms folded, his eyes gleaming down at her. 'That depends,' he said. 'There's a condition.'

Fury boiled inside her. She took a deep, ragged breath and said between her teeth. '*You can go to hell!*' She flung the door wide and brushed past him and almost ran back to her cabin, as his laughter followed her.

Barbara was preparing for bed. She looked up in surprise as Cass stormed in and shut the door with a snap behind her, surveying the flushed cheeks and brilliant eyes.

'What's happened to you?' she asked. 'You look as though you've just had a flaming row, or else been thoroughly kissed.'

'*Both!*' Cass snapped, before discretion got the better of her.

Barbara sat down on her bed, her eyes alight with curiosity. 'My boss?' she asked. 'That is where you went, isn't it? To Lucien's caravan?'

'Yes,' Cass admitted reluctantly. 'It wasn't a personal visit,' she added hastily.

Barbara grinned. 'Sounds as though it turned pretty personal,' she commented. 'I had an idea the boss-man fancied you.'

'Well, he can take his fancy somewhere else!' Cass said viciously. She flung aside her pillow and snatched up her pyjamas, heading for the shower.

'Don't you fancy *him*?' Barbara asked her retreating back.

'Not if he was the last man on earth!' Cass lied, and shut the door firmly behind her.

When she came back into the room, Barbara was reading in bed. Cass climbed into her own bed, and looked across at the other woman. 'Barbara,' she said, 'you won't mention it to anyone, will you?'

Barbara looked up. 'Discretion is my middle name,' she said. 'Otherwise I wouldn't have been working for Lucien for four years. I wouldn't dare breathe a word. Want to tell me about it?'

Cass shook her head. 'It didn't mean anything. He was just trying out an idea for the film.'

'Oh. I can see why you got mad. And I don't blame

you. He's a very singleminded brute when he's working
on a film—though in between times he's really quite
human.'

'I'll believe you.'

Barbara laughed. 'No, really! He's been good to me.
And don't look like that,' she added severely. 'He's
never fancied *me*!'

'Sorry,' Cass murmured.

'No, it's all right. I have a son—he's at boarding
school, but last year he got glandular fever, and Lucien
told me to take as much time off as I needed to look
after him until he got over it completely. We were in
the middle of filming, and I know it would have been
better from his point of view to get a replacement for
me, but he didn't. He kept my job open.'

'I don't suppose he could have got anyone as good
as you. He didn't want to lose you.'

'Oh, dear!' Barbara shook her head, smiling. 'I can
see you're off him at the moment. I'll say no more.'

Cass lay down and tried to sleep. Even after Barbara
switched off the light, it wasn't easy. Her lips tingled
with the remembrance of Lucien's mouth on them, and
her body grew warm as it had under his caressing
hands. And then she recalled the cool light of calculation in his eyes just before he kissed her, and grew
cold again. She hadn't really been a woman to him at
all, in that moment—just an experimental subject that
might help him to decide how to plan his beastly film.
He had wanted to test the view that she and Odette
had put to him, and she just happened to be handy at
the time. Almost any woman would have done.

In the morning Cass watched as they filmed a sequence
with Odette and Ethan on the beach. It was supposed
to be taking place after the woman, Ruth, had come on

the convict leader while he was fishing from the rocks. The two of them sat in the shade of one of the blossoming pohutukawas, the spent flowers all about them splashing in the sand, and as they talked it became obvious that Ruth was obliquely inviting the man to make love to her. The man's lines showed that he despised her for it, but the scene ended with him pulling her down on the sand in a torrid embrace.

Cass had seen Odette arguing passionately with Lucien before shooting began, and when she walked over to the shaded spot her face was mutinous, but as the cameras began rolling, she switched with lightning speed to a sensuous, determined woman, flaunting herself deliberately before the man, and allowing a fleeting triumph to cross her face when at last he was goaded into passion.

They went through it five times before Lucien was satisfied, and Cass watched him curiously, wondering at the hard detachment in his face while he supervised, time after time, another man making violent love to the woman everyone supposed to be his mistress.

It was all make-believe, of course, the businesslike audience and the proximity of the cameras making Cass wonder how anyone could convey any genuine emotional feeling to such a public and unromantic atmosphere. But time and again the sexual tension was built up between the two principals, until the air seemed to throb with it, and when the man hauled the woman roughly into his arms, a fury of desire seemed to leap between them, the kisses they exchanged authentically intimate. Yet all Lucien seemed concerned with were the camera angles and the placing of the actors' bodies as they sank back on the sand, the angle of Odette's head when Ethan lowered his against her throat and let the camera see her face.

At last Lucien said, 'Cut. Okay, everybody, that was fine, thanks.'

The crew relaxed, grinning, and Ethan picked himself up off the sand, and helped Odette up. She threw back her long hair, shaking sand out of it, and Lucien said quietly, 'Okay, Odette. Now we'll do it your way.'

She shot a surprised look at him, arrested with her hands in her hair, and her lovely face upturned. 'Are you serious?' she asked him.

'I'm not promising to use it,' he warned. 'Come on, make-up!' He turned, and the make-up man hurried forward. 'Get her tidied up for another take.'

The lines and the action were the same, and Ethan played his part exactly as before, but Odette invested the whole scene with a subtly different atmosphere. She delivered her lines more hesitantly, sat more stiffly and didn't lean towards the man in the blatant manner that she had used in the first several takes. It seemed as though she had nerved herself to approach him, and as though she might get cold feet at any time and retreat after all. As she spoke of her husband, and their desperate circumstances, instead of colouring her voice with contempt, she sounded pathetic and·frightened, stumblingly trying to tell Denning that she was asking for a protection that the older man could not give her. And at the last, when the camera was supposed to linger in close-up on her face, she showed on it an expression of bleak resignation.

It was a brilliant performance, and when Lucien called, 'Cut!' Cass clasped her hands together because she had a strong urge to applaud. When she heard several members of the crew do so, though, she joined in, knowing it was a very rare tribute for a film performer to receive.

Lucien didn't join in. He was standing with one hand

on the nearest camera, the other on his hip, staring thoughtfully at the ground.

Odette, smiling slightly, went up to him and queried, 'Well? Do we shoot it again?'

He looked up and put out a hand to touch her cheek. 'Could you do it better than that?'

Odette shook her head. 'I gave it all I've got.'

'Yeah, well, you've got a lot,' he admitted. 'You're one terrific actress, honey.'

'Thanks.' She kissed his cheek and smiled at him.

'All right,' said Lucien, with a hint of grimness, but his eyes were warm. 'I still haven't made a decision, one way or the other. I told you, no promises.'

'You're the boss.' She turned away with a teasing look over her shoulder, and laughed when he said, 'Huh!'

Some of the crew chuckled, too, at the exchange. Cass felt a tightness close about her chest. Odette and Lucien understood each other very well, and there had been a light intimacy about that little dialogue. Surely it must be true that they were lovers. Which made his conduct of last night even more contemptible.

They broke for lunch, and Cass covertly watched Lucien chatting with Odette and Ethan as he ate. She had to get a chance to talk to him. He couldn't have meant what he said last night about a 'condition', she decided. He had just been having a little cruel fun at her expense.

She saw him move to the table to put down his empty plate, and immediately she went to his side. Her voice firm and brisk, she said, 'Lucien, about that interview, I do need it, of course. Could you spare a few minutes now? We *are* leaving tonight.'

'Tonight?' He looked vaguely surprised.

'We've been here five days.'

'How are you going?'

'Well, Rudy will send a car. But I can't give him a time until I've done the interview with you.'

'Stay for tonight,' he said. 'I'll take you back to Auckland tomorrow morning. I've got to pick up some gear.'

'We wouldn't want to trouble you——'

'No trouble. And if you want that interview, you stay tonight. I'm going to be busy the rest of the day.'

He turned away and left her standing. Cass seethed quietly, trying not to show her annoyance in her face. Lucien had her in a cleft stick and he knew it. She had to get something from him to print, and if he said he wouldn't talk until tonight there was nothing she could do about it. She would have to phone Rudy and tell him that she and Robby had a lift tomorrow, and would see him the following day.

CHAPTER NINE

THE afternoon was spent filming a scene where the Maori war party descended on the convicts, creating a tense situation. The Maori extras, their faces and bodies adorned with imitation *moko* tattoos, and brandishing long *taiahas* or spears, and the sharp-edged hand weapons called *meres*, looked chillingly menacing. It was hard to believe, later, that these were the same young men who lounged about the grass and the verandah steps dressed casually in jeans and tee-shirts, laughing and teasing one another about their parts in the film, and strumming pop tunes on the guitars some of them had brought with them.

A group of them retained their make-up and costumes of short kilt-like flax *maro*, because Lucien wanted to film the opening of a *hangi* that had been put down earlier in the day, in the traditional manner.

The 'warriors' grumbled goodnaturedly about having to remove the earth from the ground-oven with the primitive tools of their ancestors instead of a modern metal spade, but once the cameras began rolling, they fell to the task with a will. Soon steam could be seen rising through the green leaves covering the food, and when those were removed and the pork, kumaras and fish lifted out and placed on the leaves, a delicious aroma made many mouths water. One camera was moved close for a shot of the still-steaming hot stones at the bottom of the pit, which had been heated hours before by a roaring fire before the food and a sprinkling of water was added, and the *hangi* covered.

Then Lucien signalled the end of filming, and everyone was allowed to sample the 'props'.

Paper plates were brought out, in lieu of more leaves, and the Australian crew members moved forward, intrigued, for their first taste of *hangi*-cooked food, in most cases. The atmosphere was convivial, and the evening rapidly developed into a party, with guitars providing music, while everyone sang and some even danced on the grass at the edge of the sand.

Cass kept an anxious eye on Lucien, remembering he had promised her an interview. He sat beside Odette, who seemed more relaxed than usual, laughing and singing along with the rest, while her co-star at her other side clapped in time to the music and eventually dragged her to her feet to dance with him.

Lucien grinned after them, then he, too, stood up and strolled over to where Cass was leaning against a humped root of pohutukawa.

'This shindig may last the rest of the night,' he told her. 'We could slip away to my caravan now, if you like.'

'I'll call Robby,' she said, straightening away from the tree.

Lucien's brows rose a little. 'What on earth for? He must have dozens of shots of me at work. I hardly think a static photo of a man at a table will add anything to the article. Come on.'

His hand closed about her wrist, not hard, but very firmly. They walked away from the light of the driftwood fire that had been lit by the *hangi* pit, and the sounds of revelry faded slightly as they entered the darkened camp.

'I need a notebook,' said Cass. 'And tape recorder, if you don't mind.'

Lucien shrugged. 'I'll wait for you.'

She switched on the light in the cabin, and found what she needed. She would have liked to renew her lipstick and run a comb through her hair, but Lucien was waiting outside the open door. She switched off the light and joined him, hesitating at the foot of the two steps, because the darkness now seemed very deep.

He grasped her arm lightly to guide her, and ushered her into his caravan before him.

As she stood just inside the doorway, he didn't turn on the central light, but instead went to the table and switched on a reading lamp. The table had been cleared, she could see, and he indicated it and asked, 'Want to put the recorder here?'

She did so, and sat down on the divan at one side. The caravan was quite roomy, but the space seemed enclosed and intimate. The light was a bright pool on the table, but the rest of the caravan remained dim.

'Drink?' Lucien asked.

'If you want one,' Cass answered evenly, concentrating her attention on finding a blank page in her notebook. She heard him pouring, and after a moment he placed a glass before her, on the table. He sat down opposite her on the matching divan, and propped his back against a couple of cushions in one corner. He looked at the pencil poised in her hand, his mouth slightly sardonic. 'Okay,' he said. 'What do you want to know?'

She asked him first why he had decided to film in New Zealand.

'Because the story is based on a true incident. The action starts in Australia, so it's a slice of Australian history, and as such the script appealed to me tremendously. But the bulk of the action takes place in New

Zealand, and this is where I have to film it. No one here was interested in doing this story—it's no skin off anyone's nose. And it can't harm any of your own films in the overseas market. The more exposure of your wonderful scenery, the better.' He stopped, awaiting her next question.

Having done her homework, Cass was able to ask a few intelligent questions about the other films he had directed. He was frank about the first one and its faults, but conceded that it had taught him a lot, and went on to explain what he strove for in making a film. 'Impact, authenticity and integrity,' was how he put it.

Cass looked up at that. 'Can you explain that further?' she asked. 'What do you mean by "integrity", for instance?'

Lucien emptied his glass, and looked down at it for a moment. 'I suppose—craftsmanship.'

'Not art?' she queried.

'Ah,' he said. 'You see, I have this theory that art is a function of craftsmanship, not the other way about. I find films made on the premise of art for art's sake usually fail.'

'You mean, commercially?'

'Not only commercially. On an artistic level, as well.'

'So you don't strive for artistic effect?'

'Lord, no! That would be the kiss of death for most of the films I've made.'

'What about *The Lonely Peak*?' she asked him. 'That was regarded very highly, as a work of art, wasn't it? The critics called it visually outstanding.'

'You've been reading the reviews?'

'Obviously. I have to admit I didn't see the film.'

'Because the public stayed away in droves.'

'Is that why you stopped making "artistic" films and

settled for craftsmanship—and popularity?'

Lucien looked at her in silence for a moment, his expression unreadable. Then he said, 'If you like.'

She had expected him to rise to her challenge and defend himself against the veiled suggestion of commercialism. She was conscious of a vague dissatisfaction when he didn't.

He put his glass down on the table and sat back again, his pose even more indolent than before. 'You haven't touched your drink,' he reminded her.

She didn't particularly want it, but she picked up the glass and sipped at it before she replaced it.

'What do you hope for from this film you're making now?' she asked him.

'Success.'

He sounded bored. Trying to rouse his interest, she asked, 'Why did you let Odette do the scene her way, at last, this morning?'

'Odette is a very persistent lady. And I don't want her any more strung up than she is. She lives on her nerves when she's filming.'

'You mean it was just to keep her happy? You're not going to use it?' Cass felt inordinately disappointed.

'I didn't say that, did I?' he countered mildly.

'*Are* you going to use it?' she asked point-blank.

'I don't know yet—I haven't seen the rushes. It will create problems if I do.' She looked at him questioningly, and he explained, 'If that scene is played as she wants it, the following sequences will have to be re-thought as well.'

'So—they haven't been shot yet, have they?'

'No.'

'Well then, where's the problem?'

'The problem is whether it's going to make a better film to change the interpretation of the woman's character. Odette acted magnificently this morning. But it's going to be more difficult for her to convey a change from a frightened woman desperately trying to save herself by any means, into a strong-minded lady determined to forge her own destiny. I've been arguing that the story line makes more sense if she had an eye to the main chance from the beginning.'

'But wouldn't it make a more satisfying film if the character changes and develops as the story unfolds? Otherwise, it's just a series of events, manipulated to varying degrees by the characters.'

'You could be right. And since when did an interviewer become a devil's advocate?'

'Sorry. I've become involved, I'm afraid, through watching you making the film. I didn't mean to start telling you your job.'

He smiled slightly in acknowledgement of the apology. 'Have you finished asking questions? Because I've had enough of answering them.'

Cass smiled back and switched the tape recorder off. 'Can I ask for one more comment on this film?' she said, pencil poised.

'That's calculated to make the most fluent speaker dry up, or start talking inanities,' he drawled. 'Do you always ask that?'

Cass laughed. 'Always,' she said. 'I learned early that a good many of my subjects had prepared some pithy comment that I never gave them a chance to trot out. It was dreadfully disappointing if I never asked for it.'

He laughed, too, his head thrown back a little, showing his tanned throat. 'Just say I reckon we've done a good job, and I hope the public will think so too.'

'What about the critics?'

'The critics don't pay for their tickets.'

Her pencil stopped flying across the page, and she looked up into his eyes, seeing the sardonic humour in them. 'You sound very cynical,' she commented. 'Are you serious? The money is all that matters?'

'Don't put words in my mouth. That isn't what I said.'

'But isn't it what you meant?'

'I thought you'd finished with questions.'

Cass bit her lip in frustration. Often when a subject thought the interview was finished, he relaxed and came up with some better material than in the interview proper. She was used to it, and found that they seldom minded if she quoted the 'post-interview' remarks. She would, of course, have asked permission. 'Don't you mind if people think you're more interested in money than in that "integrity" you talked about?' she asked him.

'I don't mind what people think of me,' he said. 'And I'm not about to bare my soul for the delectation of your readers. The film can stand on its own merits. As far as I'm concerned this article of yours is merely a means of bringing it to the attention of the public, so that they can see it and judge for themselves.'

'But you don't want them judging you?'

After a brief pause, Lucien said, 'That's right.'

She looked at him with speculation, as she closed her pad. 'You're a harsh judge of others,' she said. 'Are you as hard on yourself?'

'Harsh?'

'Yes. Do you deny it?'

'Much good it would do me,' he said mockingly. 'Have you and Odette been letting your hair down about me?'

Cass shook her head. 'I speak from personal experience,' she reminded him with a hint of bitterness.

She stood up, and he reminded her, 'You haven't finished your drink.'

'I don't want it, thank you. Thanks for the interview.'

She gathered up the recorder with her pad and pencil, and made to pass him on her way to the door. He stretched out a hand and, hardly moving from his lounging position on the divan, held her fast.

'Where do you think you're going?' he asked softly.

Cass tried to pull her hand free without success. 'The interview is over,' she pointed out. 'I'm going back to my cabin.'

'Oh, no. We had a bargain, you and I.'

Her heart lurched. 'Don't be ridiculous!' she snapped. 'Let me go!'

Lucien reached out his other hand and took the recorder and notebook from her and placed them on the table. The pencil rolled on to the floor, but he took no notice. 'A bargain,' he repeated. 'You don't really think I'm going to let you wriggle out of it, you little cheat?'

'I'm not a cheat! I never accepted——' she broke off with a cry of shock as a swift jerk on her imprisoned wrist brought her tumbling across his knees, and his arms came about her to hold her there. '*Stop it!*' she snapped fiercely. 'You're crazy if you think——'

Roughly, he said, 'I made a condition, and you said you wanted the interview. *You*'re crazy if you think I'll let you make a fool of me a second time.'

Cass opened her lips for a furious protest, but he stopped it, swooping suddenly on her mouth with his, his kiss invading and insolent, storming her emotions in a blaze of angry desire.

She felt her head bent back against his arm, and his hands clamped her against him, reducing her struggles to impotence. The demand of his mouth on hers was inescapable, and to her utter dismay she felt a swift and terrible urge to respond to it with passion.

Perhaps Lucien felt the slackening of her rigid resistance to him. One of his hands moved to caress her back in long, slow movements, and then it slid to her waist and up to touch her breast. A shiver of pleasure ran through her as his fingers gently probed its softness, and when his thumb found the burgeoning hardness in the centre through her thin shirt, a hot shaft of desire shot through her. Shocked, she wrenched away her mouth from his and pulled at his hand.

His fingers closed over hers, and his mouth touched her cheek and throat, as she averted her face and took a gasping breath.

He murmured, 'What's the matter? Am I going too fast for you?'

'Too fast and too far,' she managed, her voice husky. 'I'm not going to sleep with you, Lucien. I'm *not*!'

He laughed softly in her ear and said, 'Pocket your pride, honey. This time I'm calling your bluff. And relax. I'm not going to rape you. I want us both to enjoy it.'

'Lucien, I——'

He stopped her mouth with his, pulling her round to face him with a firm tug at her hair. He was holding her so that she couldn't move, but his lips moved gently on her, teasing and tantalising, his tongue feathering lightly over her upper lip, his teeth gently closing on the lower one before he kissed her properly, parting her lips inexorably with his, until she felt dizzy and helplessly kissed him back, even while she moaned a protest deep in her throat. Her neck arched beneath the increased pressure of his kiss, and her body went fluid and soft in his arms, allowing him to curve her towards him, her breasts crushed against the hardness of his chest, as he pushed her down on the cushions.

His hands slid under her cotton knit shirt, and up the smooth skin of her back to her shoulder blades. She felt her weight resting on his palms, and his thumbs caressed her shoulders as he lay close to her, his body warm and hard against her softness.

He lowered himself over her, and she felt his thigh between hers as he kissed her again, his mouth persuasive and gentle, then passionate. Her shirt had ridden up about her midriff, and he moved a little, looking down at her taut body. The waistband of her jeans sat just below her navel, and he moved one of his hands and touched her there, smiling when she bit her lip on a gasp of pleasure. His hand slid to the edge of the shirt and pulled it up, and as she saw the sudden glaze of desire in his eyes, she turned her head away, her face flaming.

'They're beautiful,' said Lucien. 'Why so bashful?'

He brought down his head, and she felt his hair brush her skin, as his lips seared a path from her navel upwards. She ached with longing for the intimacy that he was leading up to. She knew that soon there would be no stopping him—or her. His mouth was in the shallow cleft between her breasts when she summoned up a reserve of will power from somewhere deep inside herself, and thrust her hands into his hair, pulling him away from her.

He gave a grunt of pain, and his hands came up to her wrists, tightening until she had to let go. He forced her wrists back on to the divan, his weight on her heavy, now, and she saw his eyes change, become hard and angry. His glance lowered mercilessly to the visible evidence of her wanton desire, lingered there insultingly, and then returned to her face. 'Playing games, Cass?' he asked softly.

'It's not a game,' she managed, trying to steady her breathing. 'I said I won't sleep with you, Lucien, and I meant it.'

'The hell you did! Do you think I don't know that you want me, too? What are you doing? Cutting off your nose to spite your face?'

'What I'm doing is telling you I don't want you for my lover. You said you wouldn't force me.'

She met his eyes with defiance in hers. Her resolve was strengthening, the raging tide of desire quieter now, though the blood was still rushing quickly through her veins.

'Why not?' he demanded. 'Why Halliday, and not me?'

Cass closed her eyes, wincing away from the frustrated accusation in his eyes. Wearily, she said, 'You won't believe that Halliday was lying, will you?'

'Are you telling me that you didn't let him make love to you?'

'I didn't. I've never had a lover in my life.'

For a moment he was silent. Then he said, his voice silky, 'Would you like to prove it?'

Her head jerked as she faced him again, her eyes wide with shocked fury. '*No*, damn you. I would *not*!' she said chokingly.

He smiled grimly, his eyes still on her face. Then suddenly he released her wrists and in a quick, lithe movement got off the divan and stood looking down at her. When Cass hastily pulled her shirt down, he laughed a little, and her lips tightened as she swung her feet to the floor and smoothed back her tumbled hair. Her hands were shaking with reaction, and she couldn't look at him.

She made to stand, but with a hard hand on her shoulder, Lucien thrust her back and pushed her unfinished drink into her hand. 'Drink it,' he ordered tersely. 'You look as though you need it.'

She gulped it down, and it did steady her a little.

Suddenly he asked abruptly, 'Why should Hal lie to me?'

'I don't know,' Cass answered tiredly. 'Male vanity, I suppose. You were jumping to conclusions, and he *had* made a heavy pass. I guess he didn't want you to know that he hadn't got anywhere with me.'

Again he was silent. She glanced at him, and saw him frowning abstractedly. She put down the empty glass and stood up, picking up her pad and the tape recorder. The pencil had disappeared, probably under the divan. She couldn't be bothered hunting for it. All she wanted now was to get out of here.

'I'll see you back,' he said.

Cass momentarily closed her eyes. 'Please, no,' she said dully. 'I'd rather go alone.'

'Cass?' Lucien queried, as she opened the door. 'Do I owe you an apology?'

She gave a little choke of slightly hysterical laughter. 'Several, I believe,' she said. 'But don't let it worry you. All I ask is that I never set eyes on you again.'

She meant it. At that moment she felt nothing but a vast emptiness, a sort of numb despair. It didn't seem to matter whether Lucien believed her or not. She didn't care any more. Nothing mattered. When she got back to the darkened cabin she didn't bother switching on the light, but groped her pyjamas out from under the pillow, had a quick wash and crawled into bed. She didn't even cry, but lay staring into the darkness and listening to the distant sounds of the party still going on down near the beach, until sleep finally brought a welcome oblivion.

In the morning she steeled herself to meet Lucien, to sit in the car with him while he drove her and Robby back to Auckland.

She needn't have worried. He was nowhere to be seen, and Barbara said he had been struck by an idea for a scene to be shot the following day, and gone off with the chief cameraman to try its feasibility. Barbara was to drive them instead. Cass swallowed an unexpected dismay and smiled brightly as she packed her things into the estate wagon and climbed in beside Barbara, while Robby and his cameras occupied the back. Apparently Lucien was prepared to take her at her word. Or he had simply become so absorbed in his idea for the next day's shooting that he found it more important than anything else at the moment. He had probably shrugged off last night's episode as a minor defeat, and unimportant.

Robby was dropped off at his home first, and he and Susie insisted on giving Barbara and Cass a cup of tea in the fresh, newly painted kitchen of their neat home. Cass admired the colour scheme and Susie teased her husband about the problems he had encountered while he did the job. The two little boys climbed over their father in turns, and Cass thought what a happy family they were and found an unaccountable ache in her throat, making it difficult for her to swallow the home-made chocolate cake Susie had pressed on her.

When Barbara dropped her off at her flat before going to collect the gear that Lucien wanted, Cass unpacked grimly, and dumped her notes on the small table holding her portable typewriter, where she worked when she was doing copy at home. Her inclination was to leave it and find something else to do, but Rudy wanted the finished article within a few days. She might as well make a start and get it over with.

She roughed out some notes, and played back the tape of the interview with Odette, transcribing the passages she wanted to quote. She played other tapes, too, gathering the various interviews and notes into a coherent whole. She worked steadily until six, when she took a break and watched the television news, then made herself a toasted sandwich and a cup of coffee.

By working like a demon, she had the first rough draft of the article virtually done, except for the director's comments. She switched off the television and turned to the table, selected a tape and slipped it into the machine. Lucien's voice invaded the quiet room, and Cass picked up a pencil, pulled her notes towards her and blindly made a mark on the paper with shaking fingers. She heard her own voice asking a question, and as Lucien replied, the paper shimmered before her eyes, and she bit her lip fiercely and shook her head, fighting the tears.

This was ridiculous. She couldn't be breaking her heart over a man who had walked out of her life years ago, and walked back in again for a brief week, and each time had not even bothered to say goodbye. He didn't give a damn for her, and she was *not* going to give in to this terrible racking self-pity, this futile longing for his touch, his smile, his understanding. He didn't understand her, and he didn't want to. He might have briefly wanted her, once or twice. But that had nothing to do with the kind of close, loving feelings that were shared by couples like Robby and Susie, the kind of feelings that made something lasting and valuable out of a natural attraction between a man and a woman.

And that was what she wanted, not a fleeting relationship without a future, but something solid and permanent and with a promise of even better things to come. If she could feel like this after a few kisses and a week of short periods in Lucien's company, what on earth would a fully-fledged affair have done to her? It didn't bear thinking about.

She squeezed her fists over her eyes and took up the pencil again, ran the tape back to the beginning and set her teeth. She had a job to do. Well, she was going to do it. It might tear her apart to hear his voice, and she might feel like moaning with pain as she wrote his name and quoted his words, but if he could put his work first, so could she. It was, from now on, all that she had.

CHAPTER TEN

RUDY liked the completed piece on the film, and a few weeks later it appeared in *Citymag*. Combined with Robby's handsome photographs, it occupied several pages of the issue, and also featured on the cover. Cass was complimented by several of her colleagues, and should have been happy basking in praise and a sense of achievement. Instead she found herself deeply depressed and wincing inwardly every time someone mentioned her good work.

Two days after the issue went out, she was called into Rudy's office, and stopped short when she saw that he had a visitor—Lucien.

'Come in,' Rudy ordered, quite affably for him. 'Someone to see you.'

He turned his swivel chair from side to side, and Lucien stood up from the only other chair and put her into it. She shot a quick glance at his face and found it almost impassive, quite impossible to read. She managed to say, 'Why do you want to see me? Is there something wrong with the piece I wrote?'

Rudy replied instead of Lucien. 'Nothing wrong, Cass. Just the opposite, in fact. Mr Hale wants to congratulate you.'

'Congratulate——?'

Lucien said, 'Yes, you did a good job of it. I'd like to shout you a lunch, to show that I—we—appreciate a good piece of journalism.'

'I can't——'

Rudy said, 'Yes, of course you can. I'll send the

cadet out to see that alternative school this afternoon—time she got some experience—and you can take the afternoon off.'

Lucien said, 'Thank you,' and, turning to Cass, 'When will you be ready?'

'What about Robby?' she asked, clutching at straws. 'It was his work, too.'

'I saw him outside,' Lucien said smoothly. 'He was dashing off to somewhere or other, but I managed a quick word before he went. He couldn't make lunch, unfortunately.'

She looked at him again. Had he really been going to take the two of them? she wondered. She hesitated. 'I don't know——'

Rudy gave her a ferocious frown. 'Stop dithering, girl,' he advised. 'And don't keep the nice man waiting.' He stood up and saw them to the door, and five minutes later Cass found herself out in the street with Lucien's hand at her elbow.

'Rudy recommended a place,' he told her. 'I gather it's within walking distance. Do you mind?'

'No, of course not. By the time you've parked a car in the lunchtime rush hour, you'd probably have to walk miles, anyway. You did bring a car, I suppose?'

'Yes. It's parked in the *Citymag* visitors' bay at the moment.'

They walked, his hand lightly on her arm, until he saw the sign he was looking for, and guided her up a narrow stair to a small restaurant that looked over the city buildings to the harbour with its yachts riding like toy boats in the distance, the volcanic island of Rangitoto rising behind them, and the cranes and big cargo ships nearer at hand in the port.

They had a window table, and when they had ordered Cass was able to feign an interest in the view until the waiter placed a fruit cocktail in front of her.

Lucien had been silent until now, and the air seemed to be thick with tension. She could scarcely swallow the cool mixture she spooned into her mouth. Eventually she pushed the dish away and enquired, 'How is the film coming along?'

Lucien had finished before her, and was leaning back in his chair, watching her. 'Pretty well,' he said. 'Everyone hates my guts, but they're working hard and it's shaping nicely.'

'Are you so hateful?' she asked. It surprised her. He had been quite even-tempered on the whole, when she and Robby had been on the set, and she thought that most of the cast and crew liked him.

'Apparently I have been, lately,' he said somewhat grimly. 'Odette tells me I'm like a bear with a sore head. *You* seemed to think I was fairly hateful, yourself.'

Cass's breath stuck in her throat. The waiter came and removed the empty dishes from the table, and when he had gone, Lucien said softly, '*Do* you hate me, Cass?'

'No, of course not!' Her voice shook, and her hands were tightly clenched in her lap. She still wouldn't look at him.

'You did say you never wanted to see me again,' he reminded her. 'Didn't you mean it?'

Cass shrugged, trying to sound casual. 'It was said in the heat of the moment,' she said. 'You didn't need to take it quite literally.'

He put his hands on the table, linked his fingers and stared at them. 'Cass,' he said. 'You said I owed you an apology—or several. I'm offering apologies now— for what they're worth. I'm sorry if I jumped to conclusions. I'm sorry I didn't believe you. And most of all—a bit late in the day, I admit—I'm sorry about the way I acted on the ship—before we parted.'

Surprised, she looked up then, and saw him looking grim and rather dogged. 'That's a fairly wholesale apology,' she said shakily.

'Will you accept it?'

'Yes,' she said quietly. He sounded as though it mattered, and her heart skipped a couple of beats in its normal rhythm as she heard him mutter, 'Thank you,' before the returning waiter put plates of salmon salad in front of them.

The atmosphere lightened slightly, although Cass felt absurdly nervous. She asked, over their coffee, 'Did Odette win over the playing of Ruth?'

Lucien grinned faintly. 'Yes, as a matter of fact she did.'

'I'm glad. I'm sure she was right about it.'

He didn't answer that. She felt that he still had some reservations.

When he pushed away his cup, he said, 'Rudy's given you the day off. What do you want to do?'

'You needn't feel bound to entertain me. I'm sure you didn't come to Auckland just to see me.'

'I'm supposed to go to a borrowed studio to see some of the film that's been processed. Will you come with me, and let me give you dinner?'

She hesitated. 'I'd like to see the film. But I have a date tonight.'

She sensed a coolness in him. But he said, 'Okay. I'll take you home after we've been to the studio.'

It was fascinating seeing the film of scenes she had watched as they were shot. She sat beside Lucien in the dim room, aware of his arm along the back of her seat, but knowing that his entire mind was concentrated on evaluating what was being projected on the screen before them. There were more sequences that she hadn't seen, of course. The arrival of the convicts, struggling ashore from a boat, while the remains of the ship burned against a darkening sky behind them, and the deep, mysterious density of the bush seemed to threaten them from above the beach: the descent of the chief's warriors on the convicts when Denning was killed and his head taken back to Ruth: and the final scene after Ruth had killed the chief in his sleep, and stolen away from the Maori village to trek through the bush and give herself up to authority in the form of a naval captain whose ship had been sent to track down the convicts and bring them to justice.

Cass watched intently as the woman stood on the shore in her ragged clothes, waiting for the ship's boat to reach her. The officer in the bows was smartly turned out in impeccable uniform, his face stiff and suspicious.

The officer leaped from the boat and approached the woman, who stood and waited for him. He looked uncertain, moved his hand as though to remove his hat in the presence of a lady, then thought better of it. He sternly enquired her name, and she gave an ironical little smile as she calmly gave it to him. He recited some legal formula in the King's name, and she nodded.

He asked what had happened to her companions, and showed a faint shock and pity when she replied unemotionally that they were all dead.

'It's as well, lass, that you've decided to give yourself up,' he told her with clumsy gentleness. 'You could not have survived on your own.'

Again an odd little bitter smile fleetingly crossed Ruth's face. 'I was well enough,' she said. 'A chief took me for his woman.'

The officer looked disgusted. 'Savages!' he muttered.

Ruth said gently, 'Yes.' Her gaze moved over him, and went to the goggling, curious sailors who had manned the boat. 'Yes.' she said, with a strong thread of irony.

With rough compassion the officer said, 'I daresay you took no part in the murder of the ship's crew, lass, and, you being a woman and suffering the hardships that you have, the Governor will likely be lenient with you. Especially if you behave on the voyage back to Sydney. I could put in a good word for you.'

Cass had read the script. The way Lucien had first conceived this scene, she knew, was that Ruth had immediately summed up the officer and set herself out to gain his pity, with a silent promise of compliance if he should claim a payment for his intervention with the Governor. She had seen Lucien taking Odette and the actor through the scene, and at this point Odette had silently adjusted the slipping neckline of her dress, and smiled a subtle promise. Odette had invested the smile with a certain weariness and contempt, but the implication was that here was yet another man she would soon have twined about her little finger.

This version was different. There was no provocative sexuality now, in Ruth, but a strength born of indifference. Her stony gaze rested on the officer's face unblinkingly, and he frowned and said, gruffly, 'Come, then.'

Odette wheeled and walked before him to the boat, her back straight and her head held high. They still had their backs to the camera when they came to the boat and the officer put out a hand to help her. At his touch she jerked her arm away and climbed into the boat herself. She sat aloof in the bows, and as she turned to the camera it panned up to her face, set in an expression of determination. Her gaze passed without interest over the heads of the seven men in the boat, ignoring the officer and all of them as completely as though she was alone, as they pulled away from the shore. She looked strong and untouchable and completely in command of her destiny. The boat drew away from the shore and the camera, and gradually became smaller with distance, but the figure in the bows still dominated the viewer's attention until the reel came to a halt.

'The final credits will be run over the last few seconds of film,' Lucien told her. He didn't wait for her comment, but turned to the projectionist and asked for a couple of sequences to be run through again. Cass, however, hardly saw them. She had felt the power of Odette's performance in that last scene, and the effect was stunning. When the lights were switched on, she turned to Lucien and said, 'Odette is fantastic, isn't she?'

'Definitely,' he agreed. 'If she hadn't been I would never have let her get away with changing my concept of the film.'

She wondered with a stab of pain how much their personal involvement had been responsible for his willingness to listen to Odette. She must have been very persuasive, and perhaps, with her total dedication to her work, she hadn't been above using methods other than verbal to get her way.

'What are you thinking?' Lucien asked unexpectedly.

'Nothing. I was just wondering what it took to make

you change your mind,' she said rashly.

He frowned. 'She didn't use her feminine charm as a weapon, if that's what you're getting at,' he said. 'Odette is a professional through and through. She doesn't need to resort to cheap tricks.'

He looked grim until he dropped her off at the flat, and she was gripped by depression, trying to hold back foolish tears. She was getting out of the car when he asked, grabbing briefly at her wrist, 'Will you see me again?'

Surprise held her speechless for a moment, and she looked into his face, finding it still grim and without any hint of pleading. 'Yes,' she said, 'if you want me to.'

The corners of his mouth lifted a little, though it scarcely lightened his expression. He said, 'I'll be in touch,' and let her go.

Cass had promised to go to a party with Dave that evening. Feeling unsettled by her afternoon with Lucien, she was tempted to phone and make some excuse, but that would have been unfair to Dave, and besides, going to a party would take her mind off Lucien.

She dressed listlessly in a pretty bare-shouldered dress of soft tan-coloured chiffon, slipped her feet into off-white sandals and donned a pair of amber earrings. When Dave gave her a admiring look and told her she looked beautiful, she felt vaguely guilty, perhaps because she had not really tried. She gave him a perfunctory smile and followed him out to his car.

She had met his friends who were giving the party. They were a nice couple, and the party went with a swing. Cass was annoyed when she found herself sliding more deeply into depression as the evening went on. Everyone else was having a wonderful time, even Dave, who seemed to have no idea that she wasn't as happy as he was. Unfairly, she felt irritated by that, too. Trying to shake out of her mood, she drank more than she was accustomed to, and for a while acquired a wholly false sparkle.

The sparkle apparently fooled Dave, anyway. He responded to it with lighthearted eagerness, and when they left, their hostess eyed them knowingly and her husband made a meaningful remark that in other circumstances would have brought Cass up short. Tonight, however, it sailed over her slightly muzzy head as Dave's arm steered her firmly out the door and back to his car.

Outside the flat, he drew her into his arms with purpose, and for a few minutes she responded to his kisses, partly from affection and an odd sort of guilt, and partly because she hoped they would be an anodyne to the memory of another man's kisses, another man's arms . . .

She scarcely heard him as he began to mutter words against her throat and shoulder, between feverishly hot kisses. Only gradually the sense penetrated her consciousness. 'Cass, marry me. I love you desperately, don't make me wait . . . we'll get married, but let me make love to you . . . please, Cass . . .'

She had been floating in a world of hazy unreality, enjoying his kisses as one enjoys a mild intoxicant. When his hands became urgent on her skin, and she felt the trembling of his body as he held her, she was abruptly brought down to earth.

Shock and remorse cleared her brain on the instant, and she gently pushed him away. 'Don't,' she said, as he tried to find her mouth again with his. 'Dear Dave, please—give me a minute.' She meant to give *him* a minute to bring his emotions under some control, for she was suddenly in total command of her own. 'I'm sorry,' she said. 'I didn't realise that you felt so . . .'

'You know I've loved you for months,' he said, a little more steadily. 'You know I want to marry you. How did you *think* I felt? I've been patient, God knows. But when you look like that, and act the way you did tonight, do you expect me to keep at arm's length, and just *look* at you? I'm flesh and blood, Cass, and so are you, though you pretend otherwise, for some reason. You did kiss me back.'

'I know,' she said, distressed. 'I'm fond of you, and you *have* been patient with me——'

He made a sound of impatience. 'Fond! Is that all?' As she made to answer him, hesitantly, he said, 'All right, don't answer that now. I'm going to be away for a few days. When I come back, I want you to give me an answer. I'll call for you on Thursday, at seven.'

'Dave——'

'See you Thursday,' he interrupted ruthlessly. He kissed her briefly and hard and opened the door. 'Goodnight, Cass—darling.'

She didn't need until Thursday. She had been guilty of some muddled thinking—or of not thinking at all, she accused herself sternly. While Dave had been content to await her decision, she had let the situation drift on, half believing that she would soon be able to say yes to him, that the crazy interlude with Lucien Hale could be, if not forgotten, at least put in some kind of perspective that would allow her to ignore it and take what Dave could offer her, which was a great deal.

But seeing Lucien again had put paid to that foolish hope. There might be no future with him, though his casual suggesting of further meetings had brought a stirring of joy which she quelled with some difficulty.

She had to accept that Lucien might walk out of her life a second time as easily as he had before. And she also had to accept that while such a tenuous hope might lead to nothing at all, the way she felt about Lucien made it impossible for her to accept marriage with Dave or any other man. It would be grossly unfair to him, and even though these last weeks she had nursed a foolish desire to use him as a haven from the turmoil of emotion that Lucien had wakened in her, the time had come to break with Dave. She was only sorry for his sake that she had lacked the courage and the intelligence to do so sooner.

She didn't expect to hear from Lucien very soon, but on Thursday, she was told a man was on the phone for her and she lifted the receiver expecting to hear Dave's voice. She experienced a shock of surprise when Lucien's deep tones said, 'Cass? I'm in Auckland. Can I pick you up after work?'

Holding back the rush of gladness at the sound of his voice, she said, 'Thank you. But I'm not free this evening.'

After a second's silence, he said, 'I have to go back to the location tonight. I was hoping to take you to dinner first.'

'I'm sorry.'

'Look, I know it's short notice. You're not just punishing me for taking you for granted, are you? I didn't know until this afternoon that I'd have any free time tonight.'

'I had already made arrangements for tonight. I can't go out with you.'

'Can't you cancel your arrangements?'

She scarcely even thought about that. Of course she couldn't put Dave off. He wanted his answer tonight, and even though she wasn't able to give him the one he would have liked to hear, she owed it to him not to keep him dangling any longer.

'No, I can't,' she said firmly.

'Is it a man?'

'Yes.'

'The same one as last time?' Lucien asked.

'As a matter of fact, yes.'

'Keeps you busy, doesn't he?'

He sounded nasty, Cass detected the note of jealousy in his voice, and that might have softened her if she hadn't felt so keyed up with the strain of knowing she would have a difficult interview with Dave tonight, and now the disappointment of having to turn Lucien down. She thought furiously that he could hardly expect her to wait about on the offchance that he might have time to call her or take her out to dinner. 'You're pretty busy yourself,' she retorted.

There was a pointed silence. Then he said evenly, 'Put him off, this once, Cass.'

'No.' Her voice was tight with the effort of defying him. But she couldn't give in to him. She would despise herself if she did.

'I'll pick you up after work, anyway,' he said, and she heard the receiver being replaced with a force that made her wince.

She met him with her head high and her mouth very firm, because she suspected he would try again to get her to change her mind. He asked, 'Can I buy you a drink on the way?'

Cass shook her head. 'If you want a drink, I'll give you one at the flat. The pubs are too crowded at this hour, and I have to get ready. Dave is calling for me at seven.'

'So I'd better be on my way before then,' he said dryly. 'I can take a hint. Dave who?'

'Does it matter?'

'Perhaps not. How long have you been seeing him?'

'Nearly a year.'

He shot her a keen glance. 'That's a long time. It's serious, is it?'

'Look, I don't want to talk about——'

'*Is it serious?*' he demanded between his teeth, making her sit up and stare at him, rigid with startled anger. It was the anger that made her snap, '*Yes*, he's asked me to marry him!'

He stopped for a traffic light, his foot hitting the brake so hard that only her safety belt prevented her from hurtling forward.

'Sorry,' he muttered, his frowning gaze on the traffic threading across the intersection before them. The light turned green and he drove on for a few minutes before he asked, 'Are you going to marry him—this Dave?'

Cass could have said no, but some sense of what she owed to Dave prevented her. She had treated him shabbily enough, without informing someone else that she was turning him down before she had told Dave himself.

'I can't tell you that.'

'You mean you don't know?' Lucien sounded derisive.

'I mean I'm not going to discuss it with you,' she said. 'It's none of your business.'

He drove in silence the rest of the way, and when he stopped the car outside the flat he said, 'I'll take a raincheck on the drink, thanks. Are you seeing Dave on Sunday?'

Cass shook her head.

'I'm free all day Sunday,' he said. 'Can we spend it together?'

The tension and anger of the last half hour disappeared. She smiled at him, almost leaned towards him in her eager acceptance. 'Yes,' she said, 'I'd like that very much.'

He looked faintly surprised, before he asked, 'What time would suit you?'

'I go to church at nine, as a rule. Would half past ten be all right?'

'Fine. I'll see you then.'

'Shall I bring a picnic lunch?'

'If you'd like to picnic, yes. It sounds a good idea.'

Cass went inside feeling almost lighthearted, except for the aching dread of having to see Dave tonight.

In the event it wasn't as bad as she had expected. Dave was taut and she was nervous and distressed, but he had braced himself for a refusal, admitting that he had realised in the last few weeks how far she was from being in love with him.

'I wish I could have made you feel the way I do,' he said sadly.

'So do I,' Cass told him. 'I know I would have been a very lucky girl if I'd married you. But it simply wouldn't be fair.'

'Maybe you're right. Love doesn't come to order, does it?'

Cass shook her head. 'I wish it did. Life would be so simple.'

Dave frowned curiously, his voice a little jealous. 'Is there someone else for you, Cass?'

Cass looked away, and he turned her gently to face him. 'I didn't know you were seeing another man.'

'I haven't been. But I've met someone—again—a man I knew briefly some years ago . . .'

'And he's special?'

She met his eyes. 'He's very special to me. But I don't know if the feeling's mutual.'

'I hope it is, Cass,' he said huskily.

'Dave, you're very generous. You're such a dear. I wish——'

'Don't. It's over. I hope some day we'll be friends, but just now—I'd rather not see you for a while. I'll take you home.'

His goodnight kiss was brief and gentle, and she knew he was exerting a lot of self-control to keep it that way. When she went in her eyes were filled with tears, and in her heart there was a deep, inexplicable anger with Lucien, because her love for him had stopped her from giving Dave what he had wanted from her—a whole heart. And she wasn't sure that Lucien wanted anything but a casual, light love affair, a few outings, a few kisses, and a session or two of deeper lovemaking if she could be persuaded to cast aside her scruples.

She still felt much the same on Sunday when he called for her. A prickle of antagonism ran up her spine when she opened the door to him and saw him standing with a hand thrust casually into the pocket of his grey slacks, the open collar of a dark blue shirt turned back from his tanned throat, and his grey eyes appraising her own cream cotton shirt and fitting fawn trousers.

She said, 'Come in,' and stepped back to let him enter. Her flatmate was still in bed after a late Saturday night party, and she waved Lucien into a chair while she collected a jersey, knotting the sleeves about her neck before picking up the picnic basket she had packed.

He rose from the chair and took the basket from her, walking ahead of her to open the door. With his hand on the knob, he paused, until she had to look up at him. His eyes were shrewd. 'What's the matter?' he asked. 'Have I done something wrong?'

'Of course not. Nothing's the matter.'

'Then smile at me?'

She gave him a Cheshire cat grin, and he pulled the door open and gave her a little slap on the seat of her trousers as she passed him. 'Sassy,' he said, catching her indignant look with a wolfish grin of his own. He grabbed her arm and said, 'Come on. It's too early yet to quarrel. We'll drive and blow away whatever's eating you.'

CHAPTER ELEVEN

'WHERE would you like to go?' Lucien asked her. 'I've got a map, but you know the area better.'

'Have you been up to the Waitakers?' she asked. 'Along the scenic drive?'

'Years ago, when I first visited New Zealand. As I remember, it was a pretty good place for getting rid of cobwebs—or moods.'

Cass smiled reluctantly. 'It is. And if that doesn't work, we can go on to Piha.'

Lucien glanced at the map. 'A beach? What's it like?'

'Beautiful, wild and dangerous.'

His mouth quirked, and his grey eyes glinted as he said, 'Sounds fun. Let's go.'

He drove out of the city virtually in silence. They had begun climbing and passed the little township of Titirangi, then taken the road that arrowed into the dense bush before he looked sideways at her and queried. 'Feeling better?'

'There's nothing wrong with me,' said Cass, but her voice was light. There was always something soothing about the bush, even driving through it, more so if one walked. The tree ferns laced their branches over the edges of the road, and here and there a stern, straight kauri reared out of the tangle of smaller trees and glossy evergreen bushes. She wound down the window and drew in a breath of cool air scented with the distinctive smell of damp leaves and green growth.

A little while later they stopped where a path led

invitingly into the forest, a small yellow sign promising to lead them to a giant kauri. They walked side by side down the narrow track, dark and slippery with dead leaves which killed the sound of their footsteps. The tree was impressive, reaching tall and grey heavenward, thrusting its tight crown through the spindly kanuka and mottled matai and slender, smooth tawa that were its neighbours. They walked around the huge trunk and speculated on its age. Cass put a hand against the cool bark and reflected that, beside the massive old tree, her problems had suddenly diminished into rather petty little troubles, in the scheme of things.

Lucien's hand came up and covered her own, warm and hard, and she looked up warily, her body tingling with the unexpected contact.

'What are you thinking?' he asked her quietly.

She might have told him he had no right to enquire, but she replied equally quietly. 'Just that something as big and as ancient as this——' she looked up at the tree '—brings things into perspective, somehow.'

Lucien glanced up, too, and said, 'I guess so.' He looked back at her, and moved, brought her captured hand down to press it against his chest, and drew her into his arms.

She went, unresisting. There was a time and place for everything, and this seemed to be it. For an instant she looked up into grey eyes that were brilliant and keen, making her own eyes widen momentarily before they closed under the compulsion of his kiss.

It was like none of the kisses that had gone before. It seemed timeless and endless, remarkably tender, remarkably delicate, with an underlying eroticism in the soft, sensuous movements of his mouth, in her spontaneous answering movements. Her hands slid from his chest to his neck and into his crisp hair, and she felt his arms tighten about her, as his mouth stilled on hers. Then he slid his hands on to her arms and pushed her away.

Cass discovered she was trembling. She pressed her lips together hard, and kept her eyes on the dark ground as his arm about her waist turned her to walk back along the path.

She felt rejected. She could feel the hard warmth of his arm behind her, the weight of his hand against her hip, and yet with every step he seemed to be walking further away from her. And she didn't know why.

Lucien seemed preoccupied as they drove on, scarcely glancing her way once, a faint frown furrowing between his brows. The kiss had been perfect, nothing less. It should have opened doors for them, brought them close so that they could talk to each other, find out where it was possible to go from here. Instead he had immediately erected a wall between them. She could feel it, knew that he had done it deliberately, that he was determined to shut her out.

They were winding down the steep hill road to Piha, looking down on the dark ironsands and the huge Lion Rock, named for its shape, that guarded the sea's edge, before Cass realised, with a jolt, what a fool she had been. She had been discounting, wilfully closing her eyes to, Lucien's probable involvement with Odette. Because, she accused herself bitterly, she had wanted to forget it, to ignore it, to pretend that it didn't exist, or was over, or was merely a figment of the film crew's imagination. Lucien's seeking her out had renewed a hope in her, a silly, baseless hope that there could be something of value between them, something more than a few kisses or a brief, sultry affair. And perhaps he had been tempted, too—tempted to make love to her, to have 'a little on the side'. But guilt had intruded, Odette had a claim on him. Possibly only a temporary one; possibly more than that, Cass didn't know. She didn't, she told herself, fierce with hurt and humiliation, care at all. She had had enough.

They ate their picnic lunch on a rise above the beach. Lucien had brought wine to go with the chicken and salad and sandwiches. Cass accepted a glass politely and shook her head when he would have refilled it.

He drank a second and third glass on his own, without comment, tossed the last chicken bone into the paper bag they were using for the scraps, and lay propped on his elbow, surveying the wild breakers that were hurling themselves at the broad sands of the beach, and the surfboard riders who flew along with them, poised on the crests.

Cass repacked the remains of the food, and sat with her legs stretched before her, leaning back on her hands, staring at the wild, spuming sea, and into the distance where the sky merged with the blue line of the horizon. They were surrounded by straight, dry grasses which grew in tufts along the shallow dunes, with scrubby lupin plants obscuring the nearer view of the beach, where family parties were enjoying the sand and sun, and teenagers sprawled their tanned limbs on shared towels or shrieked at one another as they chased bright beach balls into the water.

Cass moved restlessly, bringing up her feet to sit cross-legged, the material of her jeans tight on her thighs.

Lucien's hand on her knee was startling, an intrusion. She stiffened and, as his fingers ran along her thigh, pushed them away violently. Her head swivelled towards him, her face tight with anger as she hissed, '*Don't touch me!*'

He moved so swiftly she hardly saw it, only felt the hard jerk of his hand on her arm, and the next moment she was flat on her back against the sand, her arms pinned, and his body across hers. Her mouth opened in a gasp of shock and fury, but it was lost in his as he kissed her with fierce, hard and utterly ruthless passion.

She floundered, trying to fight him, finding it impossible. Lucien held her effortlessly, and his mouth was determined to wring some kind of response from her.

For long moments she felt nothing but fear and anger, and the near-pain he was inflicting on her lips and on her arms where his fingers bit her flesh. Then suddenly she was blindingly aware of the heat and weight of his body, of his heart thudding against her breast, the male smell of him, his breath in her mouth, and the slight rasp of his skin against hers as his mouth fought for her submission. It added up to something potent and inescapable, and in a moment of astonished abandon, she found herself kissing him back almost savagely, arching herself against him, moaning in her throat an odd mixture of desire and denial.

He was pressing her down into the yielding sand, and she felt the physical force of his passion as one of his hands came up behind her head, freeing hers to clutch at his shoulder and spread against his back.

She wanted him with a shocking fierceness, and when he wrenched away his mouth she listened to his heavy, uneven breathing with an almost cruel satisfaction. She looked into his eyes without fear, passion and triumph in hers.

'*God!*' he breathed, staring back at her, and she almost laughed at the disbelief in his face. 'Cass!'

He hadn't known she had it in her, of course. She

laughed unsteadily, and saw the dark flush of desire in his face, and laughed again until he stilled the laughter with his mouth.

This time the kiss was less fierce, his mouth as soft as her own, but it was deeper and more intimate and very heady. He broke away, casting a dark, frustrated glance at their surroundings, the flimsy screen of sparse grasses and thin lupins, and then eased his body a little to the side of her. His fingers repeated their exploration of her thigh, and he said, with deep mockery, '*Now* tell me not to touch you!'

She closed her eyes, her senses leaping to his light touch. His hand firmed at the top of her thigh, clasping the soft flesh through the cotton trousers, and she muttered unsteadily, 'Oh, Lucien! Oh, don't!'

He laughed, and took his hand away, leaning over her, watching her face intently as she opened her eyes and saw the glinting triumph in his. He touched the flare of colour in her cheeks with the back of his fingers, then put his index finger against her lips, tracing their swollen outline. 'For years I've wanted to make you feel like this,' he said.

'Rot!' she whispered, trying to retain some sanity. 'For years you forgot all about me.'

'No. Did *you* forget *me*?'

Cass tried to drag her eyes away from the compulsion of his, tried to formulate a light, lying answer. She said baldly, 'No.'

His finger slipped into her parted lips as they pursed on the word, and she bit at it gently before he withdrew it and slid his hand down until it encircled her throat, almost threateningly.

'I wanted to hate you,' he told her. 'I did hate you, for a while.'

A shiver passed over her. 'Why?'

'I don't like deceit,' he said curtly. 'And I don't like being used.'

His face was hard and his eyes glittered coldly. Cass shifted nervously, and his fingers on her throat tightened. Almost broodingly, he said, 'I used to imagine, sometimes, that I'd make love to you until you quivered in my arms and begged me to take you—and then I'd walk away.'

Her throat closed in sudden panic fear. 'Is that what this is?' she managed at last. 'Revenge?'

His hand relaxed, and began to caress her skin. 'If it was, it's boomeranged on me. I can't walk away from you, Cass. Not now. Not ever.'

The breath seemed to leave her body in a great rush. She felt dizzy, the sky spinning overhead as she looked past him at the distant blue of it. 'What do you mean?' she asked.

'I mean I want you to marry me. Will you?'

It should have been a moment of ecstasy. She had admitted to herself weeks ago that she loved this man, had never dared imagine that he might offer her a lifetime of loving. But there were still so many questions, and the uneasy feeling that there was a strange reluctance about this proposal. She said, 'What about Odette?'

Lucien's face was blank. 'What about her?'

Bluntly, she said, 'The talk is that you and she are lovers.'

He gave her a sardonic smile. 'There's always talk on a film set. I didn't think for a minute that *you*'d be likely to believe that—after the way I made love to you?'

'I don't move in your circles. You spent a lot of time in each other's company.'

'So we did. Odette is a very intense actress, as you

know. I wanted to get the best from her, and she needed to discuss the part with me, try out her ideas, absorb what I wanted from her. Of course I spent a lot of time with her.'

'I see.' Cass stirred, and he let her push away his hands and sit up. He came behind her, his hands on her shoulders, and said, 'Well?'

She licked her lips, hesitated, and said, 'You've never forgiven me for thinking that you were Lionel Halliday, have you?'

'It doesn't matter,' he said almost roughly. 'Forget it.'

'No.' She hunched away from his hands and twisted to face him.

'I think it does matter—to you. I know I shouldn't have concealed the fact that I was a journalist, I admit that I blatantly scraped an acquaintance with you because I thought you were someone else. I didn't like doing it, but I'd been threatened with the loss of my job if I didn't get an interview with Halliday, and had been told that he was violently opposed to reporters. Okay, it was dishonest. But it's the only time in my life I've stooped to anything like it. I would never do it again. Are you going to hold it against me for ever? Haven't you ever done anything, for the sake of your career, that you're slightly ashamed of now?'

His gaze became concentrated, and he said slowly, 'Yes. I wish I'd never made *The Lonely Peak*.'

Cass's eyes widened in surprise. 'But you got a lot of praise for that film!'

'I know. I thought I could salve my conscience by making it a beautiful experience, visually. But the script was meretricious, morally bankrupt junk, and I should never have consented to work on it. I wish I hadn't.'

'Then——' she said hesitantly, '——surely you can understand——?'

He smiled wryly. 'I guess I've been fooling myself. I kept hammering the fact that you hadn't been honest, that you made use of me—or tried to. I think what really stuck in my craw all these years is the fact that when you let me kiss you, and kissed me back, you were pretending.'

'Pretending!'

'You thought I was Halliday. You'd have done anything to get that interview—except, maybe, to go as far as getting into bed with him. It was that important. Maybe I'm unreasonable. I guess it's a blow at my male ego. But the fact is, I was falling in love with you, and you were fooling around, hoping to get a story, stringing me along for your own advantage. It's been done before, and from you I found it just too hard to take. You seemed so damned innocent, and so—sincere. When I found out what you were really after, I decided you were a cold, calculating bitch, and I wanted nothing more to do with you. I managed to force myself to walk off the ship by hanging on to that belief. The trouble was, you kept invading my dreams afterwards.'

'And you mine,' she said softly. 'I wasn't pretending, Lucien. I was falling in love, too. But I figured you were simply indulging in a little shipboard romance, a passing fancy. You were so much older and more experienced, and I didn't want to be loved for a little and then left. I was scared.'

He stretched out a hand and held hers tightly. 'And now?' he prompted.

'I'm not scared any more. Only—why did you ask me to marry you?'

'My darling idiot! I love you! Why the hell do you think?'

His eyes were ablaze, and she looked away from them. 'You didn't intend to, did you? After you kissed me—by the kauri, you seemed to draw down a blind. I couldn't get close to you.'

'That's when I realised that I wasn't ever going to be able to let you go. It came as something of a shock. It needed thinking about. Are you imagining I proposed to you in the heat of the moment?'

'I thought maybe you were driven to it by—well, the fact that I haven't—I wouldn't——'

'You mean, I couldn't get you any other way?' He looked amused. 'After what happened here a few minutes ago, I'm not so sure of that.'

Cass looked militant, and he laughed. 'I take it back. Allow me a little salve for my bruised ego. You do want me, don't you?'

'You know I do.'

'And I want you—not just for your beautiful body, darling, and not just for a little while, either. That's why I want to marry you, so that I'll have all of you, and give you all of me, in all the days and nights to come, for the rest of our lives.'

She looked at him, then, steadily and frankly. 'I want that, too,' she said huskily. 'I love you, Lucien.'

'I thought you'd never say it,' he growled impatiently, hauling her into his arms, his hands hard on her back, his chin rasping gently against her cheek.

After a few moments of blissful silence and peace, he said, 'I have to go back to Australia, you know, when we finish shooting. Can we get married before that? You'll come with me, won't you? You have to—I know your career is important, but you can find a job in Australia, can't you? Or freelance, or whatever——'

'Whatever,' she agreed, laughing at his unusual anxiety. 'Whatever it takes to be near you.'

'Good.' He kissed her, and Cass pulled away and said, 'You're a male chauvinist, though, aren't you? What would you do if I'd said I couldn't give up my job?'

Immediately, he said, 'I wonder if the New Zealand film industry has a vacancy for an Australian director?'

'You wouldn't!'

'Whatever it takes,' he said, and slid his lips down her neck to the curve of her shoulder. 'This place is way too public,' he complained. 'Can't we go back to your flat?'

'If you like.' She brushed her lips across his cheek, taking an intense pleasure in the feel of his skin against her mouth. Lucien raised his head, and his eyes glittered down at her.

'Come on,' he said, and abruptly got to his feet. Cass laughed up at him as he took her hand and brought her up beside him, and for a few moments they stood with his arm about her shoulders, and hers hooked round his waist, watching the sea and the waves breaking on the dark beach. Remembering another beach where once they had kissed and walked and been at peace, Cass closed her eyes, imagining the tall palms clacking softly in a tropical breeze, the sand white and harsh with coral fragments, the soft wind bringing a scent of coconut and spice and warm lagoon waters.

'How would you fancy a tropical honeymoon?' Lucien murmured, and she opened her eyes and said, 'You just read my mind. Remember that little island?'

'I remember. I remember every moment of it.'

'We'll make some more moments like that. Years and years of them.'

'That sounds great.' He turned and picked up the picnic basket. He put it in the car and held the door for her, and as she passed him, he said in her ear, 'I can't wait to start.'

Cass laughed and got in. As he slid behind the wheel he looked at her laughing mouth and bright eyes, and asked, 'No more fears?'

'None.'

'And no need for any, I promise you.' He touched her cheek. 'Everything will be just the way you want it, I swear.'

She closed her fingers over his and held his hand tightly. 'I know.'

Lucien leaned close and kissed her gently, then started the motor and turned the car away from the sea, up the hill and into the bright promise of the future.

Harlequin Plus
A PARADISE ON EARTH

No cruise in the South Pacific would be complete without a visit to Fiji, an exotic group of islands lying approximately five hundred miles east of Australia. Fiji consists of two major islands, Viti Levu and Vanua Levu, and a smattering of smaller ones all surrounded by beautiful, but treacherous, coral reefs.

Fiji is a tropical country, and as such is very warm and often wet. In fact Suva—a major port in the largest city—gets more than 120 inches of rainfall every year! Because of this hot and humid climate, Fiji is a riot of lush, luxuriant greenery and exotic animal life.

These lovely islands are inhabited by a number of different peoples, a harmonious blend of East Indians, Chinese and of course the native Fijians; on Suva's bustling streets, saris and Western-style dresses are as common as the native *sulu* (a wraparound skirt). Such tropical diseases as malaria, which are found elsewhere in the south seas, are unknown here; and though Fiji is a very modern country with a thriving economy, it hasn't forgotten its past. Elaborate ceremonies, overseen by tribal chiefs, are still carried out, and folktales and legends are related in song and mime by lines of swaying Fijian dancers in brightly colored garments.

With its exotic landscapes and warm, welcoming people, Fiji truly qualifies as a paradise on earth—a beautiful and relaxing country that cannot fail to entrance any traveler fortunate enough to visit it.

HELP HARLEQUIN PICK 1982's GREATEST ROMANCE!

We're taking a poll to find the most romantic couple (real, not fictional) of 1982. Vote for any one you like, but please vote and mail in your ballot today. As Harlequin readers, you're the real romance experts!

Here's a list of suggestions to get you started. Circle your choice, or print the names of the couple you think is the most romantic in the space below.

Prince of Wales / Princess of Wales

Luke / Laura (General Hospital stars)

Gilda Radner / Gene Wilder

Jacqueline Bisset / Alexander Godunov

Mark Harmon / Christina Raines

Carly Simon / Al Corley

Susan Seaforth / Bill Hayes

Burt Bacharach / Carole Bayer Sager

_____
(please print)
_____
_____

Please mail to: Maureen Campbell
Harlequin Books
225 Duncan Mill Road
Don Mills, Ontario, Canada
M3B 3K9

POLL-1

4
FREE
Harlequin Romances